Official

SQA Past Papers
WITH ANSWERS

Advanced Higher
Biology

2010–2014

HODDER
GIBSON
AN HACHETTE UK COMPANY

Hodder Gibson is grateful to the copyright holders, as credited on the final page of the Question Section, for permission to use their material. Every effort has been made to trace the copyright holders and to obtain their permission for the use of copyright material. Hodder Gibson will be happy to receive information allowing us to rectify any error or omission in future editions.

Hachette UK's policy is to use papers that are natural, renewable and recyclable products and made from wood grown in sustainable forests. The logging and manufacturing processes are expected to conform to the environmental regulations of the country of origin.

Orders: please contact Bookpoint Ltd, 130 Park Drive, Abingdon, Oxon OX14 4SE. Telephone: (44) 01235 827720. Fax: (44) 01235 400454.

Lines are open 9.00–5.00, Monday to Saturday, with a 24-hour message answering service. Visit our website at www.hoddereducation.co.uk. Hodder Gibson can be contacted direct on: Tel: 0141 848 1609; Fax: 0141 889 6315; email: hoddergibson@hodder.co.uk

This collection first published in 2014 by

Hodder Gibson, an imprint of Hodder Education,

An Hachette UK Company

2a Christie Street

Paisley PA1 1NB

{BrightRED   Hodder Gibson is grateful to Bright Red Publishing Ltd for collaborative work in preparation of this book and all SQA Past Paper, National 5 and Higher for CfE Model Paper titles 2014.

Typeset by PDQ Digital Media Solutions Ltd, Bungay, Suffolk NR35 1BY

Printed in the UK

A catalogue record for this title is available from the British Library

ISBN 978-1-4718-3672-5

3 2 1

2015 2014

Introduction

Study Skills – what you need to know to pass exams!

Pause for thought

Many students might skip quickly through a page like this. After all, we all know how to revise. Do you really though?

Think about this:

"IF YOU ALWAYS DO WHAT YOU ALWAYS DO, YOU WILL ALWAYS GET WHAT YOU HAVE ALWAYS GOT."

Do you like the grades you get? Do you want to do better? If you get full marks in your assessment, then that's great! Change nothing! This section is just to help you get that little bit better than you already are.

There are two main parts to the advice on offer here. The first part highlights fairly obvious things but which are also very important. The second part makes suggestions about revision that you might not have thought about but which WILL help you.

Part 1

DOH! It's so obvious but …

Start revising in good time

Don't leave it until the last minute – this will make you panic.

Make a revision timetable that sets out work time AND play time.

Sleep and eat!

Obvious really, and very helpful. Avoid arguments or stressful things too – even games that wind you up. You need to be fit, awake and focused!

Know your place!

Make sure you know exactly **WHEN and WHERE** your exams are.

Know your enemy!

Make sure you know what to expect in the exam.

How is the paper structured?

How much time is there for each question?

What types of question are involved?

Which topics seem to come up time and time again?

Which topics are your strongest and which are your weakest?

Are all topics compulsory or are there choices?

Learn by DOING!

There is no substitute for past papers and practice papers – they are simply essential! Tackling this collection of papers and answers is exactly the right thing to be doing as your exams approach.

Part 2

People learn in different ways. Some like low light, some bright. Some like early morning, some like evening / night. Some prefer warm, some prefer cold. But everyone uses their BRAIN and the brain works when it is active. Passive learning – sitting gazing at notes – is the most INEFFICIENT way to learn anything. Below you will find tips and ideas for making your revision more effective and maybe even more enjoyable. What follows gets your brain active, and active learning works!

Activity 1 – Stop and review

Step 1

When you have done no more than 5 minutes of revision reading STOP!

Step 2

Write a heading in your own words which sums up the topic you have been revising.

Step 3

Write a summary of what you have revised in no more than two sentences. Don't fool yourself by saying, "I know it, but I cannot put it into words". That just means you don't know it well enough. If you cannot write your summary, revise that section again, knowing that you must write a summary at the end of it. Many of you will have notebooks full of blue/black ink writing. Many of the pages will not be especially attractive or memorable so try to liven them up a bit with colour as you are reviewing and rewriting. **This is a great memory aid, and memory is the most important thing.**

Activity 2 — Use technology!

Why should everything be written down? Have you thought about "mental" maps, diagrams, cartoons and colour to help you learn? And rather than write down notes, why not record your revision material?

What about having a text message revision session with friends? Keep in touch with them to find out how and what they are revising and share ideas and questions.

Why not make a video diary where you tell the camera what you are doing, what you think you have learned and what you still have to do? No one has to see or hear it, but the process of having to organise your thoughts in a formal way to explain something is a very important learning practice.

Be sure to make use of electronic files. You could begin to summarise your class notes. Your typing might be slow, but it will get faster and the typed notes will be easier to read than the scribbles in your class notes. Try to add different fonts and colours to make your work stand out. You can easily Google relevant pictures, cartoons and diagrams which you can copy and paste to make your work more attractive and **MEMORABLE**.

Activity 3 – This is it. Do this and you will know lots!

Step 1

In this task you must be very honest with yourself! Find the SQA syllabus for your subject (www.sqa.org.uk). Look at how it is broken down into main topics called MANDATORY knowledge. That means stuff you MUST know.

Step 2

BEFORE you do ANY revision on this topic, write a list of everything that you already know about the subject. It might be quite a long list but you only need to write it once. It shows you all the information that is already in your long-term memory so you know what parts you do not need to revise!

Step 3

Pick a chapter or section from your book or revision notes. Choose a fairly large section or a whole chapter to get the most out of this activity.

With a buddy, use Skype, Facetime, Twitter or any other communication you have, to play the game "If this is the answer, what is the question?". For example, if you are revising Geography and the answer you provide is "meander", your buddy would have to make up a question like "What is the word that describes a feature of a river where it flows slowly and bends often from side to side?".

Make up 10 "answers" based on the content of the chapter or section you are using. Give this to your buddy to solve while you solve theirs.

Step 4

Construct a wordsearch of at least 10 X 10 squares. You can make it as big as you like but keep it realistic. Work together with a group of friends. Many apps allow you to make wordsearch puzzles online. The words and phrases can go in any direction and phrases can be split. Your puzzle must only contain facts linked to the topic you are revising. Your task is to find 10 bits of information to hide in your puzzle, but you must not repeat information that you used in Step 3. DO NOT show where the words are. Fill up empty squares with random letters. Remember to keep a note of where your answers are hidden but do not show your friends. When you have a complete puzzle, exchange it with a friend to solve each other's puzzle.

Step 5

Now make up 10 questions (not "answers" this time) based on the same chapter used in the previous two tasks. Again, you must find NEW information that you have not yet used. Now it's getting hard to find that new information! Again, give your questions to a friend to answer.

Step 6

As you have been doing the puzzles, your brain has been actively searching for new information. Now write a NEW LIST that contains only the new information you have discovered when doing the puzzles. Your new list is the one to look at repeatedly for short bursts over the next few days. Try to remember more and more of it without looking at it. After a few days, you should be able to add words from your second list to your first list as you increase the information in your long-term memory.

FINALLY! Be inspired...

Make a list of different revision ideas and beside each one write **THINGS I HAVE** tried, **THINGS I WILL** try and **THINGS I MIGHT** try. Don't be scared of trying something new.

And remember – "FAIL TO PREPARE AND PREPARE TO FAIL!"

Advanced Higher Biology

Structure of the examination

The external assessment for Advanced Higher Biology has two components worth a total of 125 marks:

Investigation Report (25 marks)

By the time you complete the course and start revising for your examination, you will already have submitted your Investigation Report. This is marked externally and the marks awarded are added to your examination score.

Examination (100 marks)

The examination contributes 80% of the total marks and consists of three sections:

Section A contains 25 multiple choice questions (1 mark each) based on Units 1 and 2. 8–10 questions will test problem solving (PS) and practical abilities (PA), with the remainder testing knowledge and understanding (KU).

Section B contains structured questions, data handling questions and extended response ("essay") questions based on Units 1 and 2 and is worth 55 marks. 13–16 questions will test PS and PA, with the remainder testing KU.

Section C contains structured questions, data handling questions and short response questions based on each of the optional units and is worth 20 marks. 4–6 questions will test PS and PA, with the remainder testing KU. You should only attempt questions from one unit in Section C.

Some good advice!

You will have 150 minutes to tackle 100 marks, i.e 1.5 minutes per mark on average. Do not spend too long on questions you find difficult – come back later after answering easier questions that might occur.

The examination paper uses a variety of question types in a number of different topic areas. There are no half-marks in Advanced Higher Biology.

These past papers will give you plenty of opportunities to practise answering the kinds of questions that you will face in the examination.

Multiple choice questions (Section A)

Section A has 25 questions that show quite a high average score from year to year. However, you need to make sure that you do not lose any marks unnecessarily. Although the questions appear first in the paper, that does not compel you to answer them at the beginning. Anxiety at the start of the exam can sometimes lead to errors and carelessness that would not happen later, when you may be more relaxed. Consider looking

quickly through the paper to see if there are questions or topics that really suit you well that, if tackled at the start, will boost your confidence and really warm up those grey cells!

In multiple choice questions, it is important to consider all options before deciding on your answer, even if you think that "A" is correct. If you do not know an answer, you should not leave the grid blank – there is no negative marking; try to eliminate one or two options to improve your chances of guessing correctly.

Structured questions (Sections B and C)

Structured questions make up the bulk of Sections B and C. They may be very straightforward, testing simple recall, or can be much more demanding and require understanding in contexts that might be unfamiliar to you. Do not be put off by this – try to make the connections and apply your knowledge.

Understanding action verbs and doing what they require is very important. Use these papers and marking instructions to understand the tasks required when you are asked to **"name"**, **"state"**, **"give"**, **"describe"**, **"explain"**, **"account for"**, and **"discuss"**.

Read through the whole of a question quickly before formulating responses to individual items. This avoids writing too much for items that come first and ensures you include details needed for later parts of the question.

Make sure that you do not miss out questions on the reverse of the fold-out pages used for the long data-handling question.

Extended response questions (Sections B and C)

Section B has two extended response questions. The "essay" question is worth 15 marks and you can choose 1 of 2 questions. There is also a short response question (with no choice) worth 4/5 marks. About one third of the marks in Section B involve extended writing; this means that you must practise organising and writing essays. Each of the optional Units (in Section C) will also have a short response question worth 4/5 marks.

Biology has a very rich vocabulary. To help you master the subject's extensive array of technical terms, download and print a copy of the Course Specification (http://www.sqa.org.uk/files_ccc/Biology_Advanced_Higher1.pdf). Go through the syllabus, highlighting all the technical terms. Make sure that you can define and use these terms correctly.

Try to define relevant terms at the start of essays. This may gain marks and will also help you to organise the information needed for your answer. After reading the question carefully, be sure to answer it! Do not make the common error of inventing a new title for the topic being tested.

Try to avoid reverting to knowledge from earlier courses and missing out the appropriate detail for Advanced Higher. You need to show evidence of progress beyond Higher.

Look at the marks available and plan an appropriate length of answer. For example, in an essay that has only 6 marks on cell cycle and 9 on cell culture, you need to be sure you know enough detail for both parts before you choose to answer it. Do not write too much on mitosis, giving long and detailed descriptions, if only 6 marks are available for the whole of the cell cycle.

In the Unit 2 answers, it is always worth giving examples when describing relationships or adaptations.

Make and follow a plan, do not just write everything you know about a topic. There is no specific penalty for writing too much but it will reduce the time you have for answering other questions.

Data handling and problem solving

Most of the problem solving marks in Section B are to be found in the long, data handling question at the beginning. In this challenging question, worth about 13 marks, information is presented in a variety of forms that may include text, diagrams, graphs, charts and tables. There is no redundant information – everything has a purpose, either to aid understanding or to be used in answering the questions. Along with PS questions there will also be some KU questions, generally worth about 4 marks.

Stems of questions and any instructions are very carefully worded to set the level of demand. You may find: "use the data", "use information from Table 1 and Figure 2", "what evidence", "show as a ratio", "calculate", or "explain how the data supports". All of these expect candidates to collect information from graphs, tables or texts and do something. "Explain" questions are generally "A" questions that will require careful thought and expression; they may also require you to recall coursework.

If a question says "use data", then numerical values are essential in answers and possibly a calculation is required. However, do not overdo quantification when justifying a conclusion. In Advanced Higher there is little scope to reward repetitive, unnecessary picking of data; questions are constructed so that this is not required. Recognising and describing trends is more relevant and only selected key values may be expected.

Many candidates find it difficult to derive "general conclusions" from data. General conclusions require thought to *summarise* evidence and indicate trends.

Where there are complex data sets, questions guide you to the correct set; so if a question says "refer to Figure 3", the answer will be wrong if it is based on Figure 4.

The marks allocated to items will give you an idea about the amount of thought and information needed in an answer. A question valued at three marks is going to need more detailed treatment than those worth less.

Percentage calculations are often used to provide a way of standardising units for comparison. Calculations may generate decimal fractions as answers. Rounding errors are common. For example 175/13000 as a percentage is 1.346. This can be rounded to 1.3 but not 1.4 and it can be rounded to 1.35 but not 1.34.

Make sure that you can use scientific notation such as indices appropriately; e.g. knowing that 10^{10} is a hundred times bigger than 10^8.

You should automatically give units, when appropriate, in the answers to numerical questions; you may lose marks by omitting them.

Generally, in the exam, graphs and charts are presenting experimental results taken from published research papers. When no accurate numerical information is needed, the grid lines may be omitted.

Questions regularly have graphs and charts with error bars. If error bars are present there will generally be a question relating to them. You are often expected to use mean values for deciding on trends and for calculations; the role of error bars is often to judge if differences between mean values for experimental treatments are significant. If error bars overlap, then mean values are not different and a treatment had no effect. Conversely, if error bars do not overlap, the difference between mean values is revealing a treatment effect. You can also use error bars to comment on the degree of variation in measured values.

Good luck!

Remember that the rewards for passing Advanced Higher Biology are well worth it! Your pass will help you get the future you want for yourself. In the exam, be confident in your own ability. If you're not sure how to answer a question, trust your instincts and give it a go anyway. Keep calm and don't panic! GOOD LUCK!

ADVANCED HIGHER

2010

[BLANK PAGE]

X007/701

NATIONAL
QUALIFICATIONS
2010

THURSDAY, 27 MAY
1.00 PM – 3.30 PM

BIOLOGY
ADVANCED HIGHER

SECTION A—Questions 1–25 (25 marks)

Instructions for completion of Section A are given on *Page two*.

SECTIONS B AND C

The answer to each question should be written in ink in the answer book provided. Any additional paper (if used) should be placed inside the front cover of the answer book.

Rough work should be scored through.

Section B (55 marks)

All questions should be attempted. Candidates should note that Question 8 contains a choice.

Question 1 is on Pages 10, 11 and 12. Questions 2 and 3 are on Page 13. Pages 12 and 13 are fold-out pages.

Section C (20 marks)

Candidates should attempt the questions in **one** unit, **either** Biotechnology **or** Animal Behaviour **or** Physiology, Health and Exercise.

Read carefully

1 Check that the answer sheet provided is for **Biology Advanced Higher (Section A)**.

2 For this section of the examination you must use an **HB pencil** and, where necessary, an eraser.

3 Check that the answer sheet you have been given has **your name**, **date of birth**, **SCN** (Scottish Candidate Number) and **Centre Name** printed on it.

   Do not change any of these details.

4 If any of this information is wrong, tell the Invigilator immediately.

5 If this information is correct, **print** your name and seat number in the boxes provided.

6 The answer to each question is **either** A, B, C or D. Decide what your answer is, then, using your pencil, put a horizontal line in the space provided (see sample question below).

7 There is **only one correct** answer to each question.

8 Any rough working should be done on the question paper or the rough working sheet, **not** on your answer sheet.

9 At the end of the examination, put the **answer sheet for Section A inside the front cover of the answer book**.

Sample Question

Which of the following molecules contains six carbon atoms?

A Glucose

B Pyruvic acid

C Ribulose bisphosphate

D Acetyl coenzyme A

The correct answer is **A**—Glucose. The answer **A** has been clearly marked in **pencil** with a horizontal line (see below).

Changing an answer

If you decide to change your answer, carefully erase your first answer and using your pencil, fill in the answer you want. The answer below has been changed to **D**.

SECTION A

All questions in this section should be attempted.

Answers should be given on the separate answer sheet provided.

1. The following diagram represents a bacterial cell.

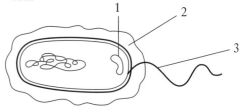

Which **one** of the following correctly identifies the structures labelled 1, 2 and 3?

	1	2	3
A	plasmid	flagellum	capsule
B	flagellum	capsule	plasmid
C	plasmid	capsule	flagellum
D	capsule	plasmid	flagellum

2. Plasmodesmata are structures that link

   A   cell walls in adjacent prokaryotic cells

   B   cell walls in adjacent eukaryotic cells

   C   cell cytoplasm in adjacent prokaryotic cells

   D   cell cytoplasm in adjacent eukaryotic cells.

3. The key below shows features of biological molecules.

   1   Soluble in water.......................go to 2
       Insoluble in water ....go to 3

   2   Extracellular............................A
       Hydrolytic...............................B

   3   Storage...................................C
       Structural...............................D

   Which letter could be both triglycerides and glycogen?

4. The diagram below shows the changes in cell mass and DNA mass during two cell cycles.

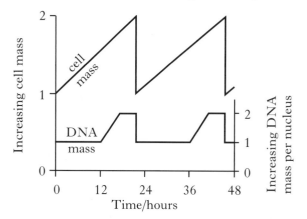

What valid conclusion could be made from the graph?

During the cell cycle

   A   interphase is the longest phase

   B   mitosis is divided into four phases

   C   replication takes place between 0 and 12 hours

   D   cytokinesis takes place at 12 and 36 hours.

5. Which line in the table below correctly describes adenine and thymine and the bonding between them in a DNA molecule?

	Adenine	Number of hydrogen bonds	Thymine
A	purine	two	pyrimidine
B	pyrimidine	three	purine
C	pyrimidine	two	purine
D	purine	three	pyrimidine

[Turn over

6. One cause of cystic fibrosis is a mutation in the CFTR gene which codes for 1480 amino acids. The most common mutation results in the deletion of one amino acid.

Which line in the table below shows correctly the number of nucleotides in the mutated gene and the number of amino acids in the protein that is synthesised?

	Number of nucleotides encoding the mutated gene	Number of amino acids in the protein synthesised
A	4431	1477
B	4439	1480
C	4437	1479
D	4439	1479

7. The diagram below shows the distribution of protein molecules in a cell membrane.

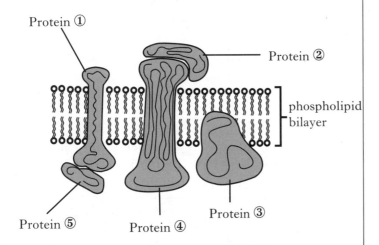

Protein ①
Protein ②
phospholipid bilayer
Protein ③
Protein ④
Protein ⑤

Which line in the table below correctly identifies a peripheral and an integral membrane protein?

	Peripheral membrane protein	Integral membrane protein
A	1	5
B	2	1
C	3	4
D	5	2

8. The diagram below shows a metabolic pathway that is controlled by end product inhibition.

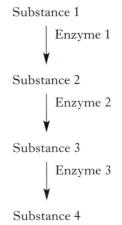

Substance 1
Enzyme 1
Substance 2
Enzyme 2
Substance 3
Enzyme 3
Substance 4

For Substance 4 to bring about end product inhibition, which of the following will it interact with?

A   Substance 1

B   Substance 3

C   Enzyme 1

D   Enzyme 3

9. Covalent modification of enzymes is used to control their activity.

Which of the following processes involves the covalent modification of an enzyme?

A   The conversion of trypsinogen into trypsin.

B   The end-product inhibition of phosphatase.

C   The allosteric inhibition of glycogen phosphorylase.

D   The conversion of sucrose into glucose and fructose.

10. Which of the following acts as a hydrophobic extracellular signalling molecule?

A   Insulin

B   Testosterone

C   Acetylcholine

D   Cholesterol

11. The following stages are involved in amplifying DNA fragments using the polymerase chain reaction (PCR).

V   DNA denatures

W   Primers bind

X   Complementary DNA strands replicated

Y   Temperature changed to about 75 °C

Z   Temperature changed to about 55 °C

After heating the fragments to about 95 °C, which of the following sequences occurs?

A   X, Z, V, Y, W

B   Z, V, W, Y, X

C   V, X, Z, W, Y

D   V, Z, W, Y, X

12. A piece of DNA 20 kilobase pairs (kbp) long was digested using different restriction enzymes. BamHI, EcoRI and PstI. The results are shown in the table below.

	Restriction enzyme used			
	PstI	BamHI	EcoRI	BamHI PstI
Lengths of DNA fragments (kbp)	15	17	12	12
	5	3	8	5
				3

Which of the following set of fragments would result if all three enzymes were used together?

A   7, 5, 3, 2

B   8, 7, 3, 2

C   12, 3, 2

D   9, 5, 3, 3

13. A certain restriction enzyme will only cut a DNA strand between two Cs when the base sequence CCGG is present.

Two homologous segments of DNA that carry different alleles of a gene are shown below. Allele 2 has a single base-pair difference.

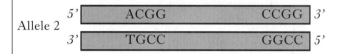

Allele 1 was treated with the restriction enzyme and the fragments *w*, *x* and *y* were obtained and separated by gel electrophoresis. The resulting band pattern for allele 1 is shown below.

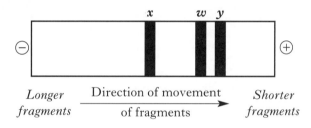

Which of the following band patterns would result when the procedure was repeated using allele 2?

14. Several species of bacteria have been found deep under the Pacific Ocean, where hot water escapes from the sea bed.

In these marine ecosystems, the bacteria can use hydrogen sulphide as an energy source to fix carbon dioxide into organic molecules. When the bacteria break down, organic material is released, which filter feeders consume.

This information indicates that the bacteria are

A   heterotrophs

B   detritivores

C   autotrophs

D   decomposers.

15. Three pyramids of numbers are shown below.

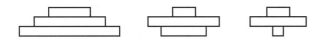

Which of the following food chains **cannot** be represented by any of these pyramids?

A   Oak tree → leaf miner → tree warbler

B   Algae → pond snail → nematode parasite

C   Grass plants → rabbit → stoat

D   Phytoplankton → zooplankton → herring

16. The table below shows data obtained from an investigation into the mass and population density of some organisms in a heathland food web.

Which line in the table shows correctly the species with the highest biomass per square metre?

	Species	Mean mass of organism (g)	Population density (numbers m^{-2})
A	cricket	0·10	4
B	ladybird	0·03	20
C	aphid	0·002	5420
D	weevil	0·005	3250

17. The diagram below shows the nitrogen cycle.

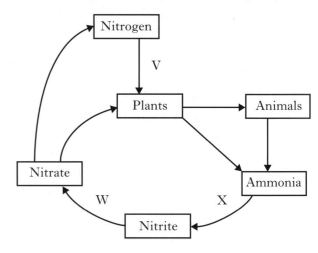

Which line in the table below correctly identifies the micro-organisms involved at the stages shown?

	V	W	X
A	Nitrosomonas	Nitrobacter	Rhizobium
B	Rhizobium	Nitrobacter	Nitrosomonas
C	Nitrobacter	Rhizobium	Nitrosomonas
D	Rhizobium	Nitrosomonas	Nitrobacter

18. The table below shows four examples of interactions between species.

Which column in the table shows correctly the benefits (+) or costs (−) which result from each interaction?

Interaction	A	B	C	D
Sheep grazing in a field of grass	+/−	+/−	+/+	+/−
Owls and foxes hunting for the same food	+/−	−/−	−/−	+/−
Corals acting as hosts for zooxanthellae	+/−	+/+	+/+	+/+
"Cleaner fish" feeding on parasites which they remove from other fish	+/+	+/+	+/−	+/+

19. Anolis lizards are found on Caribbean islands. They feed on prey of various sizes.

Histogram 1 shows the range of prey length eaten by *Anolis marmoratus* on the island of Jarabacoa, where there are five other Anolis species.

Histogram 2 shows the range of prey length eaten by *Anolis marmoratus* on the island of Marie Galante, where it is the only Anolis species.

Histogram 1: Jarabacoa Island

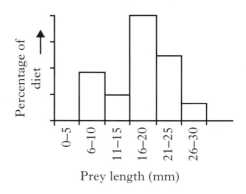

Histogram 2: Marie Galante Island

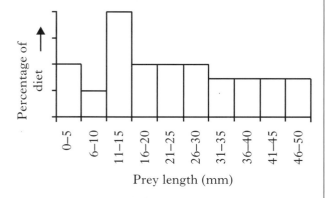

Which of the following statements could explain the different range of prey sizes eaten by *Anolis marmoratus* on the two islands?

A   Larger numbers of prey are found on Marie Galante.

B   *Anolis marmoratus* occupies its fundamental niche on Jarabacoa.

C   *Anolis marmoratus* occupies its realised niche on Marie Galante.

D   Resource partitioning takes place on Jarabacoa.

20. Each statement below applies to either conformation or regulation.

1   A wide range of habitats can be occupied
2   A restricted range of habitats can be occupied
3   There is a high energy cost
4   There is no energy cost

Which statements apply to conformation?

A   1 and 4

B   1 and 3

C   2 and 4

D   2 and 3

21. The figure below shows the general relationships between the internal environment and variation in the external environment of four animals.

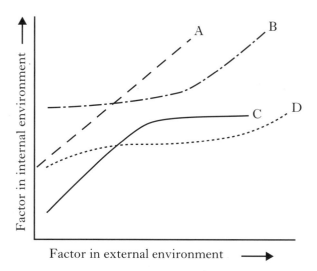

Which animal is the most effective regulator?

[Turn over

22. Eutrophication can result from agricultural activity.

    Which of the following defines eutrophication?

    A   Algal bloom

    B   Increased BOD

    C   Loss of diversity

    D   Nutrient enrichment

23. The figure below represents part of an aquatic food web.

    P1 and P2 are producers.

    C1, C2 and C3 are consumers.

    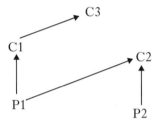

    Analysis of a persistent organic pesticide in this ecosystem produced the following results:

    Result 1 P1 has a higher concentration of the pesticide in its tissues than is present in the surrounding water.

    Result 2 C2 converts the pesticide into a more toxic chemical in its tissues.

    Result 3 The concentration of the pesticide in P1 is lower than that in C1 which, in turn, is lower than that in C3.

    Which row in the table shows the processes responsible for Results 1, 2 and 3?

	Result 1	Result 2	Result 3
A	bioaccumulation	biotransformation	biomagnification
B	biomagnification	biotransformation	bioaccumulation
C	biotransformation	bioaccumulation	biomagnification
D	bioaccumulation	biomagnification	biotransformation

24. The insecticide DDT is metabolised in birds to DDE. The level of DDE in eggs affects the shell thickness. Premature egg breakage begins when mean shell thickness is 80% of normal.

    The graph below shows how DDE content of the diet affects DDE content of eggs and mean shell thickness.

    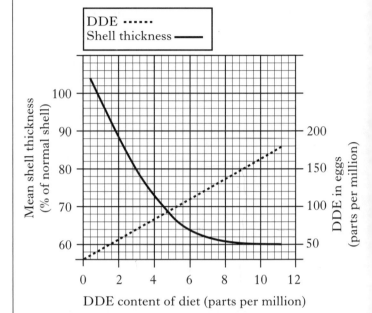

    What would be the minimum DDE concentration to cause the start of premature egg breakage?

    A   150 parts per million

    B   70 parts per million

    C   9 parts per million

    D   3 parts per million

25. Succession which follows the clearing of long-established farm land is described as

    A   allogenic

    B   secondary

    C   degradative

    D   primary.

[END OF SECTION A]

Candidates are reminded that the answer sheet MUST be returned INSIDE the front cover of the answer book.

[Turn over for Section B on *Page ten*

SECTION B

**All questions in this section should be attempted.
All answers must be written clearly and legibly in ink.**

1. Proto-oncogenes code for proteins that stimulate cell division. When these genes mutate they can become oncogenes and cause the excessive cell proliferation associated with tumour formation.

   A recent study investigated a chromosome mutation discovered in lung tumour cells. The mutation is a rearrangement of two genes on the same chromosome, resulting in the fusion of the two genes (Figure 1). The genes are *EML4*, which is involved in microtubule formation, and *ALK* which codes for a kinase enzyme. As a result of this fusion, a new protein is formed that has uncontrolled kinase activity inside the cell.

   Figure 1 : Formation of the EML4–ALK fusion gene

   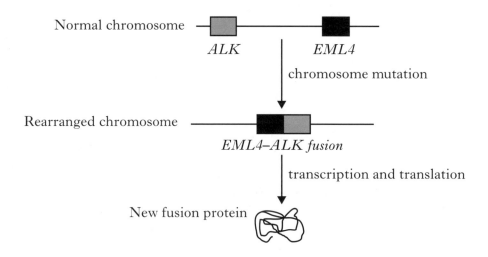

   Part of the study aimed to find out if normal cells are transformed to divide abnormally after treatment with the fusion gene. In the treatments, genes were introduced into normal cells that were then cultured in a flat dish containing a suitable growth medium. Abnormal cell division is indicated by the transformed cells stacking up in multiple layers called *foci*.

   The four gene treatments used are shown in the Table. In the fourth, the *EML4–ALK* fusion gene was modified so that the kinase produced was inactive.

   Table: Results of cell transformation study

Gene treatment	Formation of foci
ALK alone	no
EML4 alone	no
EML4–ALK fusion	yes
EML4–ALK fusion modified	no

Question 1 (continued)

The study also investigated the possibility that kinase inhibitors could be used to treat tumours arising from the fusion gene. The growth of normal and transformed cells suspended in liquid culture was monitored in the presence and absence of a kinase inhibitor. The results are shown in Figures 2 and 3.

Figure 2: Effect of kinase inhibitor on normal cells

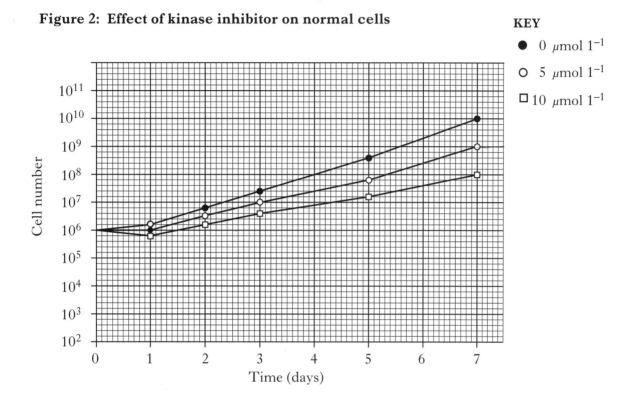

Figure 3: Effect of kinase inhibitor on cells transformed with *EML4–ALK*

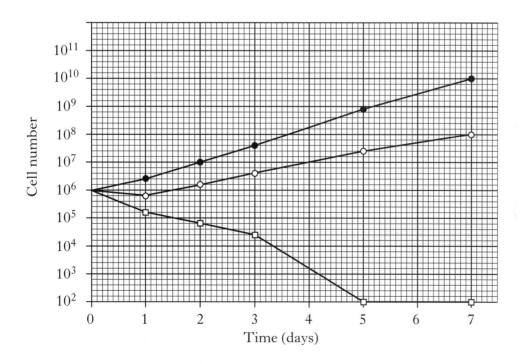

[Question 1 continues on *Page twelve*

Marks

Question 1 (continued)

(a) State why abnormal proliferation of cells can occur when only one copy of an oncogene is present.   1

(b) (i) In the study, abnormal cells formed *foci*. Describe the appearance of a culture of normal animal cells that have stopped dividing.   2

(ii) Give a reason for adding fetal bovine serum to cell culture medium.   1

(c) Refer to the table. Explain how the results show that:

(i) the chromosome rearrangement created an oncogene;   1

(ii) the effect of the fusion gene is uncontrolled kinase activity.   2

(d) Use data from Figures 2 and 3 to show that normal and transformed cells are capable of dividing at the same rate.   1

(e) Refer to Figures 2 and 3.

(i) Show that the $10\,\mu\mathrm{mol\,l^{-1}}$ inhibitor concentration reduces the proliferation of normal cells by a factor of 100.   1

(ii) What general trend is observed for the growth of cells when the concentration of inhibitor is varied?   1

(iii) Use data from the $5\,\mu\mathrm{mol\,l^{-1}}$ concentration to show that transformed cells are more sensitive to the presence of the inhibitor than normal cells.   1

(f) The study aimed to find a possible therapy for tumours caused by fusion mutation. How do the results suggest that $10\,\mu\mathrm{mol\,l^{-1}}$ of inhibitor would be the most useful to test on patients?   2

    (13)

[Questions 2 and 3 are on fold-out *Page thirteen*

Marks

2. The cell wall of the prokaryote *E. coli* is made of a substance that consists of polysaccharide chains cross-linked by short chains of amino acids. The polysaccharide is made up of two kinds of sugar: N-acetylmuramate (NAM) and N-acetylglucosamine (NAG). NAM and NAG alternate along the chain and differ from glucose only at the C2 and C3 positions.

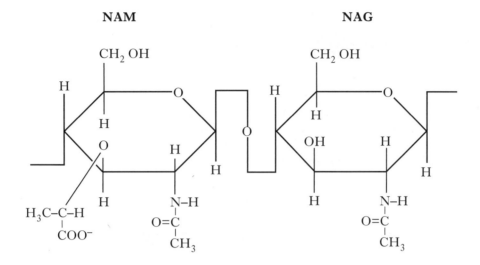

(a) Name the substance that makes up the cell wall of *E. coli*.   1

(b) NAM and NAG are joined by a glycosidic bond.

   (i) Explain why this bond is described as β(1–4).   2

   (ii) The enzyme lysozyme damages bacterial cell walls by breaking the bonds between NAM and NAG.

     What type of reaction is catalysed by lysozyme?   1

                                                                                           (4)

3. Describe the transport of sodium and potassium ions across the plasma membrane.   **(5)**

Marks

4. Transgenic plants can be produced using genetically engineered plasmids. The plasmids are obtained from bacteria that naturally infect plant cells. A modified plasmid is shown in the diagram below.

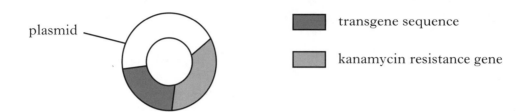

plasmid

■ transgene sequence

□ kanamycin resistance gene

Bacterial cells containing the modified plasmid are incubated with plant cells. The plant cells are then cultured in a growth medium containing kanamycin.

(a) What is meant by the term transgenic?　　1

(b) Name the bacterial source of these plasmids.　　1

(c) Explain the role of kanamycin in the production of transgenic plants.　　2

(d) Give **one** example of the use of this transgenic technology.　　1

(5)

Marks

5. Bramble plants (*Rubus fruticosus*) are pollinated by a variety of nectar-feeding insects, such as the meadow brown butterfly (*Maniola jurtina*). Bramble flowers are one of many nectar sources for this species.

A study focused on competitive interactions occurring between meadow browns and other insects at bramble flowers. The average time a meadow brown spent feeding when not disturbed by another insect is shown in the bar graph at A. The other bars show its feeding duration when another insect was also present.

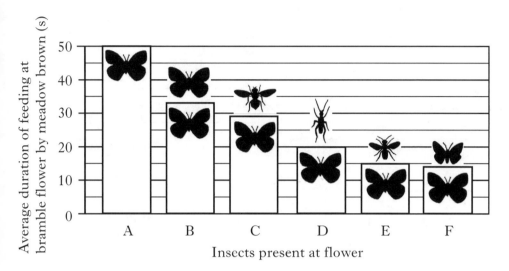
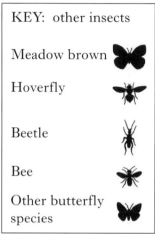

(a) Explain why intraspecific competition is expected to be more intense than interspecific.   1

(b)   (i) Which bar represents intraspecific competition?   1

     (ii) Give **one** general conclusion that can be drawn from these data about competitive interactions at bramble flowers?   1

(c) From the information provided, state why the relationship between meadow brown butterflies and bramble plants is not an example of mutualism even though there are benefits to both species.   1

         (4)

[Turn over

Marks

6. A laboratory experiment investigated the decomposition of beech (*Fagus sylvatica*) leaves following four different treatments. Fresh leaves were either left to form leaf litter or were fed to herbivorous caterpillars to form caterpillar faeces. The mass losses of these samples were then compared with and without the detritivore activity of woodlice.

Figure 1 shows the four treatments carried out. Figure 2 shows the mass loss of the four samples produced over a twelve week period.

Figure 1

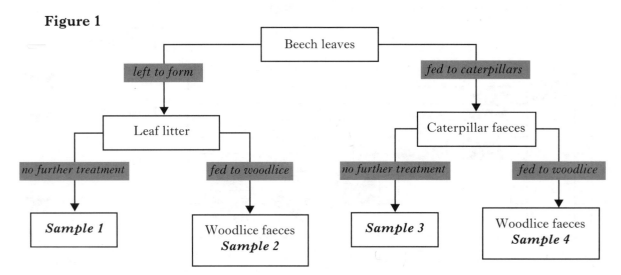

Figure 2

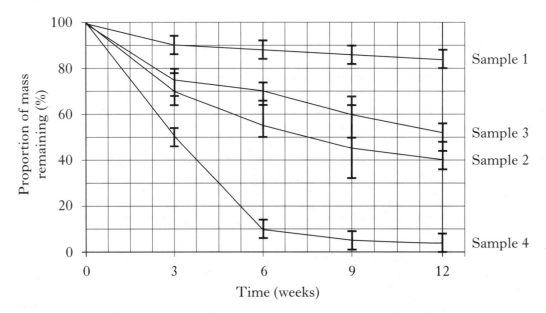

(a) How do the diets of herbivores and detritivores differ?   1

(b) Refer to Figure 2.

    (i) What evidence is there that leaves passing through the guts of two invertebrates decompose more than seven times faster than leaves allowed to form leaf litter?   2

    (ii) Use the error bars to comment on the results obtained for Samples 2 and 3 after 9 weeks.   1

    (iii) Explain why Sample 4 shows the most rapid loss in mass.   1

    (5)

Marks

7. (*a*) Explain how the level of pollution in an ecosystem could be monitored using changes in population.   **2**

(*b*) The widespread use of the drug diclofenac to treat cattle in the Indian subcontinent has led to a rapid decline in the populations of various species of vulture. For example, in 2008 the population of the oriental white-backed vulture (*Gyps bengalensis*) was estimated to be 11 000, a decline of 99·9% since 1992. Although diclofenac has low persistence and generally it has low toxicity, vultures are now known to be unusually susceptible to it.

    (i) What was the population of *Gyps bengalensis* in 1992?   **1**

    (ii) Explain why the effect on the vulture populations is greatest when they feed on carcasses of cattle treated with diclofenac shortly before their death.   **1**

(4)

8. Answer **either** A **or** B.

  A. Increasing the rate of food production to meet global demands is challenging.

    Discuss the management of the environment for intensive food production with reference to:

    (i) control of species that reduce yield;   **7**

    (ii) monoculture.   **8**

OR   **(15)**

  B. Plants are increasingly being cultivated for biomass as an alternative source of energy to fossil fuels.

    Discuss:

    (i) energy fixation and primary productivity;   **5**

    (ii) fossil fuels and air pollution.   **10**

(15)

[END OF SECTION B]

[Turn over

SECTION C

Candidates should attempt questions on <u>one</u> unit, <u>either</u> Biotechnology <u>or</u> Animal Behaviour <u>or</u> Physiology, Health and Exercise.

The questions on Biotechnology can be found on pages 18–20.

The questions on Animal Behaviour can be found on pages 22–25.

The questions on Physiology, Health and Exercise can be found on pages 26–28.

All answers must be written clearly and legibly in ink.

Labelled diagrams may be used where appropriate.

BIOTECHNOLOGY

Marks

1. (a) Legumes interact with bacteria to produce nitrogenase.

    (i) Name the genes responsible for the synthesis of nitrogenase. **1**

    (ii) What chemical transformation is catalysed by nitrogenase? **1**

  (b) Sea buckthorn (*Hippophae rhamnoides*) produces fruit that has potential as a food and medicinal crop. Although not a legume, it has a symbiotic relationship in which nitrogenase is synthesised and the plant receives nitrate. When it is grown as a crop, nitrogen fertiliser is required to produce a high yield of fruit.

    The Figure below shows the effect of daily nitrate fertiliser application on nitrogenase activity in sea buckthorn root nodules over a period of 30 days.

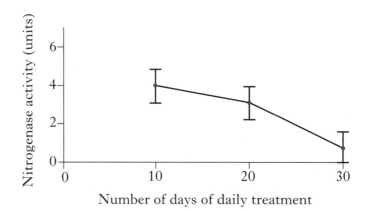

    Describe the effect of nitrate application on nitrogenase activity. **2**

(4)

2. Describe how B lymphocytes respond to foreign antigens. How is this response applied in the preparation of polyclonal sera? **(5)**

Marks

BIOTECHNOLOGY (continued)

3. Bananas are important as a crop but the planting material required is often in short supply. Scientists have developed a micropropagation system as shown in the flow chart.

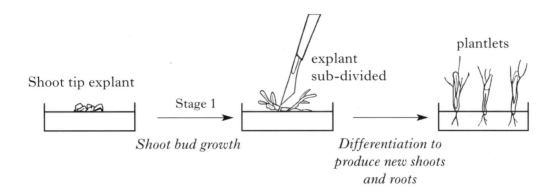

(a) Suggest **two** advantages of propagating banana plants using this system. 2

(b) State **two** environmental conditions that need to be controlled during the development of the plantlets. 1

(c) The effect of plant growth regulators on shoot regeneration in Stage 1 is shown in the table.

MS medium + growth regulators (mg l^{-1})		Explants differentiated (%)	Mean number of shoots per explant
+ IAA	+Kinetin		
0	0	29	2
0·1	1·0	42	4
0·1	2·5	46	8
0·1	5·0	58	8
0·5	1·0	54	12
0·5	2·5	66	20
0·5	5·0	58	28

   (i) What evidence is there that growth regulators benefit propagation? 1

   (ii) Use the data to explain why a growth regulator combination of 0·5 mg l^{-1} IAA + 5·0 mg l^{-1} kinetin is recommended. 1

   (5)

[Turn over

Marks

BIOTECHNOLOGY (continued)

4. (*a*) Probiotics are produced by the dairy industry to provide health benefits beyond basic nutrition.

Describe **one** such health benefit.   1

(*b*) A company that produces a probiotic yoghurt drink claims there is a measurable beneficial effect when there are at least 10^{10} viable cells of *Lactobacillus casei* per $100\,cm^3$ carton.

The Figure shows how a biotechnologist used dilution plating to check the number of bacteria in a $100\,cm^3$ carton of the drink.

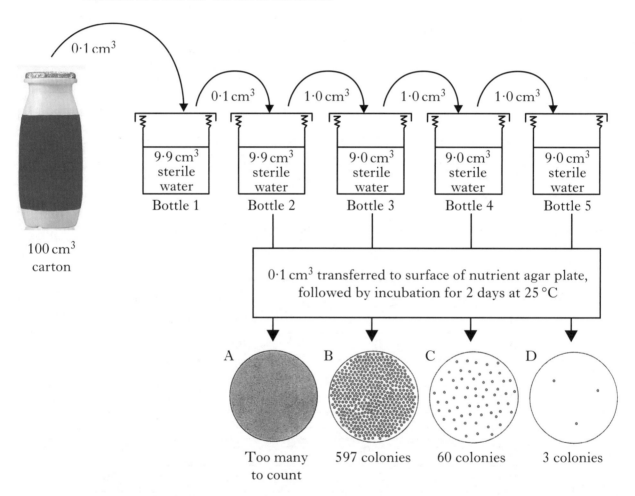

(i) Explain why dilution plating was used to check the number of bacteria rather than a direct count under the microscope.   1

(ii) Explain why sterile water was used throughout the dilution steps.   1

(iii) Explain why plate C would be selected to check the number of bacteria in the drink.   1

(iv) Use the information to show that more than 10^{10} viable cells were present in the carton.   2

(6)

(20)

[End of *Biotechnology* questions. *Animal Behaviour* questions start on Page 22]

[BLANK PAGE]

Marks

SECTION C (continued)

ANIMAL BEHAVIOUR

1. Many animals use colours and patterns to avoid predation. Some butterflies and moths, for example, have paired circular patterns on their wings.

   It has often been assumed that these wing spots are effective deterrents because they resemble the eyes of the predator's own enemies—the *eye mimicry hypothesis*. An alternative explanation suggests that the off-putting effect arises from visual contrast—the *conspicuous signal hypothesis*.

   In a recent experiment to test these hypotheses, targets made from triangular pieces of card were printed with the following patterns.

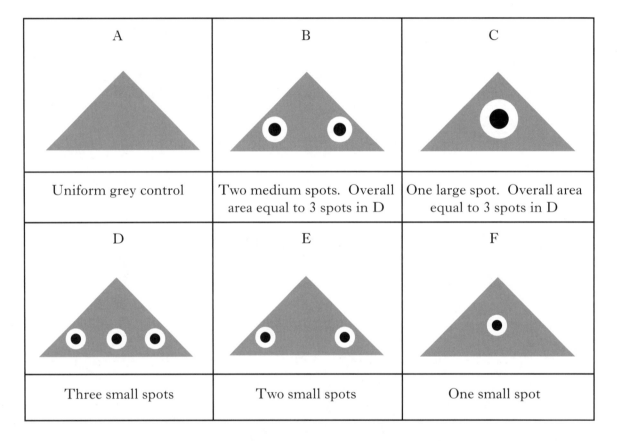

A	B	C
Uniform grey control	Two medium spots. Overall area equal to 3 spots in D	One large spot. Overall area equal to 3 spots in D
D	E	F
Three small spots	Two small spots	One small spot

   Each target had a mealworm attached to it. The targets were pinned to trees in woodland containing a variety of predatory bird species. They were checked for predation after 3, 24 and 48 hours. The survival of the mealworms indicated how successful the target patterns had been.

   (*a*) Suggest a variable that should be controlled in the placement of the targets.　　**1**

   (*b*) With which target would there be least predation if the eye mimicry hypothesis is correct?　　**1**

Marks

ANIMAL BEHAVIOUR (continued)

1. (continued)

(c) The table below shows mealworm survival for each target following bird predation.

Target	Survival (%)		
	At 3 hours	At 24 hours	At 48 hours
A	65	8	2
B	95	45	21
C	97	48	20
D	93	35	12
E	88	30	8
F	90	25	6

Explain how the results support the conspicuous signal hypothesis.   2

(d) Name **one** other defence strategy where colour or pattern are used to avoid predation.   1

     (5)

2. Describe the benefits obtained by primates living in hierarchical groups.   **(4)**

[Turn over

Marks

ANIMAL BEHAVIOUR (continued)

3. Three-spined sticklebacks (*Gasterosteus aculeatus*) are fish widely distributed in rivers, lakes, ponds and estuaries throughout the British Isles. During the breeding season, from March to July, the male's throat and belly become a brilliant orange-red and his eyes electric-blue.

(a) In observations of breeding sticklebacks, a checklist of different actions may be used to help in the analysis of their behaviour.

What name is given to such a checklist?   1

(b) The breeding coloration of red throat and blue eye is found in male sticklebacks but not in females.

(i) What term is used to describe this difference between males and females?   1

(ii) State why the male's coloration is important in courtship.   1

(c) A wild, outbred population of sticklebacks was captured and inbred for two generations. The table below shows the effects of inbreeding on some aspects of reproduction in these sticklebacks.

Population	Fertilisation rate (%)	Hatching rate (%)
Wild/no inbreeding	98	94
One generation inbred	95	90
Two generations inbred	84	78

(i) Describe briefly how an inbred population could be produced.   1

(ii) How can these results be explained?   2

(6)

Marks

ANIMAL BEHAVIOUR (continued)

4. (a) The graphs below show survival of fruit flies (*Drosophila melanogaster*) from a normal-learning strain and a high-learning strain produced by artificial selection.

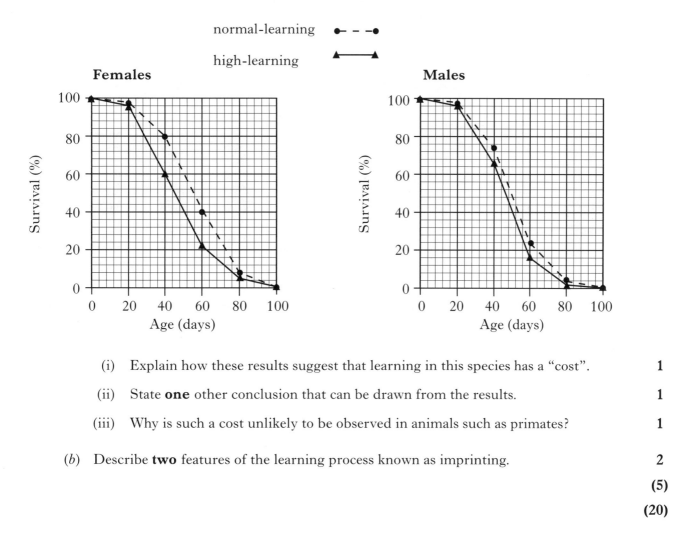

    (i)   Explain how these results suggest that learning in this species has a "cost".   1

    (ii) State **one** other conclusion that can be drawn from the results.   1

    (iii) Why is such a cost unlikely to be observed in animals such as primates?   1

(b) Describe **two** features of the learning process known as imprinting.   2

      (5)

      (20)

[End of *Animal Behaviour* questions. *Physiology, Health and Exercise* questions start on Page 26]

[Turn over

Marks

SECTION C (continued)

PHYSIOLOGY, HEALTH AND EXERCISE

1. The Figures below show cardiac data for men between 18 and 34 years old who undertake different periods of sports training per week.

Figure 1   **Figure 2**

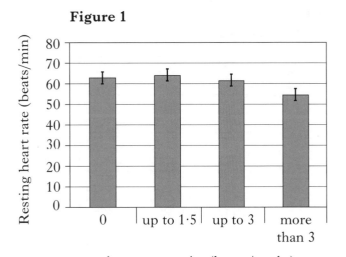

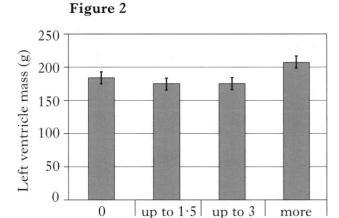

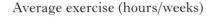

(a) Use information from both Figures to show that the "athletic heart" is an effect of prolonged training.   2

(b) What other information would be required to determine cardiac output?   1

(c) What is meant by the term *cardiac hypertrophy*?   1

(d) Give **one** example of a cardiovascular health benefit that could arise from exercising for less than three hours per week.   1

                                                                              (5)

2. Describe the role of insulin in maintaining glucose balance and explain how non-insulin dependent diabetes mellitus (NIDDM) arises.   **(5)**

Marks

PHYSIOLOGY, HEALTH AND EXERCISE (continued)

3. The daily intake of calcium for different age groups of females was compared with the recommended intake level. The results shown in the Figure below indicate that actual intake exceeds the recommended level only up to the age of eight.

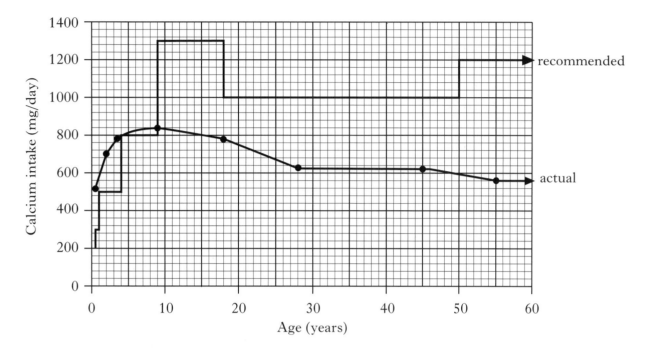

Explain why a high level of calcium intake is recommended for:

(*a*) the 9 to 18 age range;

1

(*b*) the over 50s.

2

(3)

[Turn over for Question 4 on *Page twenty-eight*

Marks

PHYSIOLOGY, HEALTH AND EXERCISE (continued)

4. (*a*) Direct calorimetry is an accurate but expensive way to measure human energy output.

   Indirect calorimetry uses measurements of oxygen consumption to estimate energy expenditure.

   (i) Describe how energy expenditure is measured by direct calorimetry.   2

   (ii) What **two** aspects of breathing must be measured during indirect calorimetry?   2

   (*b*) It is assumed that a person on a "mixed food" or average diet will release 20·20 kJ of energy for one litre of oxygen used. This energy value is described as the *energy equivalent of oxygen*.

   (i) A typical individual uses 41·5 litres of oxygen walking slowly for an hour.

   How much energy does this activity expend?   1

   (ii) The "average diet" has been worked out so that the energy equivalent of oxygen value it gives is reasonably accurate whatever a person's diet contains.

   The table below lists values for the energy equivalent of oxygen when the diet is made up of a single food.

Food	*Energy equivalent of oxygen* (kJ)
Starch	21·18
Glucose	20·97
Fat	19·67
Protein	19·25

   Use the data to show that the value for an average diet is accurate to within 5% of any diet based on a single food.   2

   (7)

   (20)

[END OF QUESTION PAPER]

ADVANCED HIGHER

2011

[BLANK PAGE]

X007/701

NATIONAL QUALIFICATIONS 2011	WEDNESDAY, 1 JUNE 1.00 PM – 3.30 PM	BIOLOGY ADVANCED HIGHER

SECTION A—Questions 1–25 (25 marks)

Instructions for completion of Section A are given on *Page two*.

SECTIONS B AND C

The answer to each question should be written in ink in the answer book provided. Any additional paper (if used) should be placed inside the front cover of the answer book.

Rough work should be scored through.

Section B (55 marks)

All questions should be attempted. Candidates should note that Question 8 contains a choice.

Question 1 is on Pages 10, 11 and 12. Question 2 is on Page 13. Pages 12 and 13 are fold-out pages.

Section C (20 marks)

Candidates should attempt the questions in **one** unit, **either** Biotechnology **or** Animal Behaviour **or** Physiology, Health and Exercise.

Read carefully

1   Check that the answer sheet provided is for **Biology Advanced Higher (Section A)**.

2   For this section of the examination you must use an **HB pencil** and, where necessary, an eraser.

3   Check that the answer sheet you have been given has **your name**, **date of birth**, **SCN** (Scottish Candidate Number) and **Centre Name** printed on it.

     Do not change any of these details.

4   If any of this information is wrong, tell the Invigilator immediately.

5   If this information is correct, **print** your name and seat number in the boxes provided.

6   The answer to each question is **either** A, B, C or D. Decide what your answer is, then, using your pencil, put a horizontal line in the space provided (see sample question below).

7   There is **only one correct** answer to each question.

8   Any rough working should be done on the question paper or the rough working sheet, **not** on your answer sheet.

9   At the end of the examination, put the **answer sheet for Section A inside the front cover of the answer book**.

Sample Question

Which of the following molecules contains six carbon atoms?

A   Glucose

B   Pyruvic acid

C   Ribulose bisphosphate

D   Acetyl coenzyme A

The correct answer is **A**—Glucose. The answer **A** has been clearly marked in **pencil** with a horizontal line (see below).

Changing an answer

If you decide to change your answer, carefully erase your first answer and using your pencil, fill in the answer you want. The answer below has been changed to **D**.

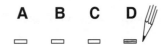

SECTION A

All questions in this section should be attempted.

Answers should be given on the separate answer sheet provided.

1. Cellobiose is a disaccharide with glucose monomers joined by a β 1, 4 bond.

   Which of the following represents cellobiose?

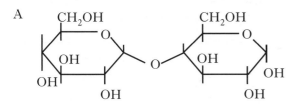

   A

   B

   C

   D

2. The following stages occur during the culture of mammalian cells.

   W   Cells flatten

   X   Cells divide

   Y   Cells become confluent

   Z   Cells adhere to surface

   Which line below shows the correct sequence of stages?

   A   X→W→Y→Z

   B   Z→W→X→Y

   C   Z→Y→W→X

   D   X→Y→Z→W

3. A piece of plant tissue prepared for growth under tissue culture conditions is known as

   A   a callus

   B   an explant

   C   a protoplast

   D   a hybrid.

4. The graphs below show the effect of plant growth substances on the development of roots and shoots in plant tissue culture.

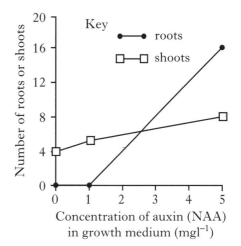

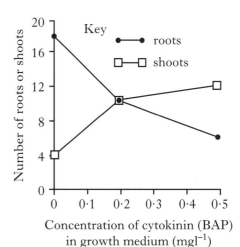

   Which of the following treatments produces a root : shoot ratio of 2 : 1?

   A   0·2 mgl^{-1} BAP

   B   0·5 mgl^{-1} BAP

   C   2 mgl^{-1} NAA

   D   5 mgl^{-1} NAA

5. In the formation of fats, which type of linkage is formed by the dehydration (condensation) reaction between glycerol and a fatty acid?

   A   Phosphodiester

   B   Glycosidic

   C   Peptide

   D   Ester

6. Which of the following describes the structure of guanine?

   A   A purine base with a single-ring structure

   B   A purine base with a double-ring structure

   C   A pyrimidine base with a single-ring structure

   D   A pyrimidine base with a double-ring structure

7. An average diploid human cell contains 6×10^9 base pairs of genetic code. Only 1·5% of this may be coding for protein.

How many base pairs code for protein in a human gamete?

   A $4\cdot5 \times 10^7$

   B $9\cdot0 \times 10^7$

   C $4\cdot5 \times 10^8$

   D $9\cdot0 \times 10^8$

8. Which of the following is responsible for cell-cell recognition?

   A   Glycoprotein

   B   Phospholipid

   C   Hormones

   D   Peptidoglycan

9. The sodium–potassium pump spans the plasma membrane. Various processes involved in the active transport of sodium and potassium ions take place either inside the cell (intracellular) or outside the cell (extracellular).

Which line in the table correctly applies to the transport of potassium ions?

	Binding location of potassium ions	*Conformation of transport protein*
A	intracellular	not phosphorylated
B	extracellular	phosphorylated
C	intracellular	phosphorylated
D	extracellular	not phosphorylated

10. Covalent modification can be used to regulate enzyme activity.

Which of the following is an example of covalent modification?

   A   Allosteric modulation

   B   End product inhibition

   C   Binding of an inhibitor to the active site

   D   Addition of a phosphate group by a kinase enzyme

11. The table below shows the results of an investigation into the effects of varying substrate concentration on the activity of the enzyme phosphatase in the presence of inhibitors. The greater the absorbance the more active the enzyme.

| Substrate concentration (%) | Absorbance | | |
	Inhibitor X	Inhibitor Y	Inhibitor Z
0·1	0·03	0·12	0·06
0·25	0·06	0·17	0·06
0·5	0·14	0·21	0·06
1·0	0·30	0·36	0·06

What valid conclusion can be drawn from the results?

A   An increase in substrate concentration reduces the effect of all three inhibitors.

B   All three inhibitors are competitive inhibitors.

C   Inhibitor Z has least effect on enzyme activity.

D   Inhibitor Y has least effect on enzyme activity.

12. A length of DNA is cut into fragments by the restriction enzymes BamHI and EcoRI.

BamHI cut site   ▼   EcoRI cut site   △

DNA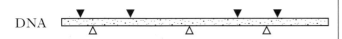

Which of the following gives the correct number of DNA fragments obtained?

	DNA cut by BamHI only	DNA cut by EcoRI only	DNA cut by both BamHI and EcoRI
A	5	4	8
B	4	5	8
C	5	4	9
D	4	5	9

13. The following diagram represents a food web.

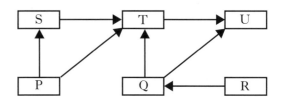

Which line in the table below correctly describes the organisms?

	Producer	Herbivore	Omnivore	Carnivore
A	P	Q	U	S
B	Q	R	S	T
C	R	S	T	U
D	P	U	T	Q

14. A river ecosystem receives about $6\,000\,000\,kJm^{-2}year^{-1}$ of solar energy. Of this energy 98% is **not** used in photosynthesis.

Which of the following shows the amount of energy $(kJm^{-2}year^{-1})$ captured by the producers in this ecosystem?

A   120 000

B   588 000

C   1 200 000

D   5 880 000

15. The percentage of energy transferred from one trophic level to the next describes

A   ecological efficiency

B   growth

C   consumption

D   productivity.

[Turn over

16. The Alcon blue butterfly (*Maculinea alcon*) spends most of its life cycle as a caterpillar associated with usually only one species of red ant (*Myrmica* species). Once the caterpillar chews its way out of the flower where the butterfly laid its eggs, it will die unless ants find it. Ants respond to the caterpillar's secretions and adopt it, taking it into their nest. The caterpillar is fed by worker ants and grows quickly, occasionally eating ant larvae.

Which of the following represents the association between the butterfly species and the ant species?

A   Commensal

B   Mutualistic

C   Parasitic

D   Predatory

17. The diagram below represents part of the nitrogen cycle.

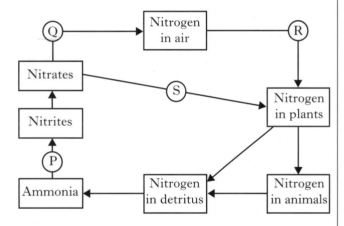

Which of the following stages is likely to involve activity of the enzyme nitrogenase?

A   P

B   Q

C   R

D   S

18. The function of leghaemoglobin is to

A   allow oxygen to react with fixed nitrogen

B   remove oxygen from nitrogen compounds

C   trap nitrogen for use in forming plant proteins

D   trap oxygen to protect bacterial enzymes.

19. The low nitrate content of a marshland soil could result from the activity of

A   *Rhizobium*

B   *Nitrobacter*

C   *Pseudomonas*

D   *Nitrosomonas*.

20. Which of the following is a density-independent effect?

A   An increase in disease decreasing the yield in a crop species

B   An increase in prey numbers increasing the abundance of predators

C   A decrease in grazing increasing the abundance of a plant species

D   A decrease in rainfall increasing the abundance of a plant species

21. The figure below shows two species of butterfly which are bright orange with black markings.

Only the monarch (*Danaus plexippus*) is unpalatable to its predators.

Monarch butterfly

Viceroy butterfly

Which type of mimicry is involved and which species is the mimic?

	Type of mimicry	Mimic
A	Batesian	Monarch
B	Müllerian	Monarch
C	Batesian	Viceroy
D	Müllerian	Viceroy

22. Some insects have a period of dormancy in which a stage of the life cycle is inactive. This type of dormancy is known as

   A   hibernation

   B   diapause

   C   aestivation

   D   symbiosis.

23. The figure below shows the general relationships between the internal environment and variation in the external environment of four animals.

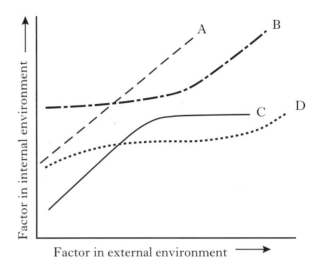

Which animal could occupy the widest range of habitats?

24. Which of the following correctly describes eutrophication?

   A   Addition of artificial fertiliser to farmland

   B   Nutrient enrichment in ponds

   C   Loss of complexity in rivers

   D   Algal bloom in lochs

[Turn over

25. Cultivation of soya beans is carried out in areas where hedgerows have been cleared to make large open fields.

The crop is regularly treated with herbicides to which soya bean plants are resistant.

Which line in the table below shows changes that would be expected to occur in an ecosystem when a soya bean farm is set up?

	Soil erosion	Species diversity	Density of insect pest species
A	increase	increase	decrease
B	increase	decrease	increase
C	decrease	decrease	decrease
D	decrease	increase	increase

[END OF SECTION A]

Candidates are reminded that the answer sheet MUST be returned INSIDE the front cover of the answer book.

[Turn over for Section B on *Page ten*

SECTION B

All questions in this section should be attempted.
All answers must be written clearly and legibly in ink.

1. *Schistosoma* is a parasitic flatworm found in tropical areas throughout the world. The flatworm can live for many years within a host. In humans, if untreated, it causes the disease schistosomiasis (bilharzia), which can be fatal.

   Schistosoma japonicum is found in East Asia; its life cycle is shown in Figure 1. The parasite's eggs hatch in fresh water, releasing a free-living stage that infects a species of freshwater snail. The parasite multiplies asexually within this secondary host before being released into the water as a second free-living stage. This stage is capable of penetrating the skin of humans and other mammals when they are in fresh water. Inside the liver of the mammal, the flatworms develop into sexually mature adults that disperse eggs via the host's large intestine.

   Figure 1: Life cycle of *Schistosoma japonicum*

   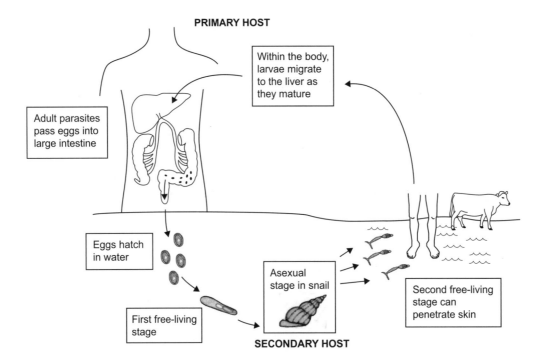

   Successful control of *Schistosoma* is very difficult. Drugs can kill flatworms inside the body but they cannot prevent re-infection. The following factors contribute to high re-infection rates: the parasite has free-living stages; the secondary host can reach high population densities very quickly; untreated, unhygienic humans act as "superspreaders".

   A trial to control *S. japonicum* near a freshwater lake in China compared two pairs of villages given different treatment programmes. Inhabitants of Ximiao and Zhuxi continued to receive the routine annual dose of a drug that kills adult flatworms. Those living in Aiguo and Xinhe were given a programme of intervention that combined the same routine annual drug treatment with the following additional strategies: relevant health education, sanitation, clean bathing water and restrictions on the access of cattle to the lakeside.

   The methods used to evaluate the effectiveness of the intervention programme are shown in the Table and the major findings are shown in Figure 2. The target set for the successful control of *Schistosoma* was to reduce infection in villagers to 1% of the population.

Question 1 (continued)

Table: Methods used to detect *Schistosoma* stages

Stage in life cycle	Detection method for stage
Asexual stage in snail	Dissection of snail samples
Second free-living stage	Dissection of mice exposed in laboratory to samples of lake water
Adult	Non-invasive assessment of human infestation

Figure 2: Infection rates in control and intervention villages

A Control Villages

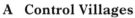
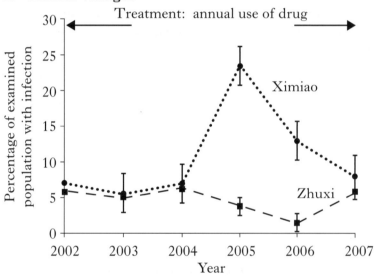

B Intervention Villages

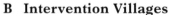
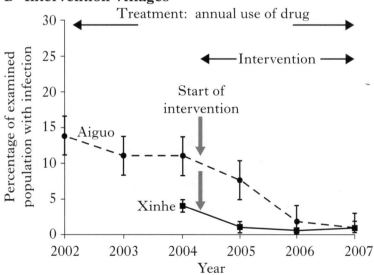

[Question 1 continues on *Page twelve*

Marks

Question 1 (continued)

(*a*) (i) Explain what is meant by the term parasitism. **2**

  (ii) *Schistosoma* has free-living stages but can only feed or reproduce when in contact with a host. What term is used to describe this form of parasitism? **1**

(*b*) One of the keys to the successful control of *Schistosoma* is to reduce the number of "superspreaders".

  (i) Suggest a "non-invasive assessment" for identifying superspreaders. **1**

  (ii) Give **two** aspects of the intervention designed to tackle superspreaders. **2**

(*c*) (i) Use the data from the trial to show that the intervention is needed to achieve the 1% target for infection. **2**

  (ii) Comment on the reliability of the results. **1**

(*d*) Attempts have been made to control *Schistosoma* through the use of molluscicides to kill the secondary host. Using the information, suggest why this method of control is unlikely to be successful with reference to

  (i) the secondary host; **1**

  (ii) the parasite. **1**

(*e*) Explain how the broad host specificity of *S. japonicum* has influenced both the design of the intervention programme and the methods for measuring its effectiveness. **3**

(14)

[Question 2 is on fold-out *Page thirteen*

Marks

2. The graph below shows variation in global atmospheric carbon dioxide concentration during a fifty year period. Seasonal variation occurs because there is much more green plant biomass in the northern hemisphere than in the southern hemisphere. The underlying trend, however, reveals an increase in concentration.

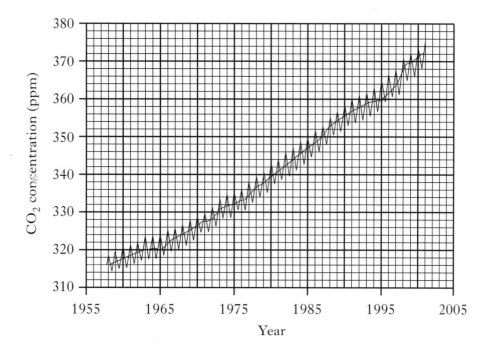

(a) Which **two** cellular processes are responsible for the seasonal variation in carbon dioxide concentration of the atmosphere? 1

(b) Using the trend line, calculate the percentage increase in the carbon dioxide concentration between 1965 and 1995. 1

(c) The increasing carbon dioxide concentration contributes to the enhanced greenhouse effect.

(i) Explain what is meant by the term *enhanced* in relation to the greenhouse effect. 1

(ii) Name a gas, other than carbon dioxide, that contributes to the enhanced greenhouse effect. 1

(4)

Marks

3. Soils that have developed from serpentine rocks have a naturally low abundance of minerals such as calcium, nitrogen, phosphorus and potassium, and a high abundance of potentially toxic metals such as nickel. The succession of serpentine plant communities shows little facilitation and is limited by the regular input of toxic minerals from the erosion of the rock. The climax vegetation that develops tends to be sparse and species present have unusual adaptations to cope with the high concentrations of metal in the soil.

   (*a*) (i) What is meant by facilitation in succession?   **1**

   (ii) What term describes a succession influenced by external factors such as erosion?   **1**

   (*b*) The flowering herb *Alyssum bertolonii* is favoured in serpentine soils because it can isolate absorbed nickel into specialised leaf hair cells. As a result, its dry mass can be as high as 3% nickel. Most other species are susceptible to nickel poisoning at much lower concentrations.

   (i) What term describes the increasing levels of nickel found in *A. bertolonii*?   **1**

   (ii) Explain why a serpentine climax community is unlikely to have many trophic levels.   **1**

   (iii) Suggest why *A. bertolonii* could be used as an indicator species.   **1**

   (5)

4. Discuss the concept of niche with reference to the competitive exclusion principle.   **(4)**

Marks

5. Myoglobin and haemoglobin are oxygen-carrying proteins. Myoglobin has one polypeptide chain and is found in muscle. Haemoglobin has four polypeptide chains and is found in red blood cells. The tertiary structures of the myoglobin and the haemoglobin chains are very similar. Each chain has one binding site for oxygen.

The proportion of binding sites occupied by oxygen is known as *saturation*.

$$\text{Saturation} = \frac{\text{number of oxygen binding sites occupied}}{\text{total number of oxygen binding sites}}$$

The graph shows the binding of oxygen to haemoglobin and myoglobin as the available oxygen is increased.

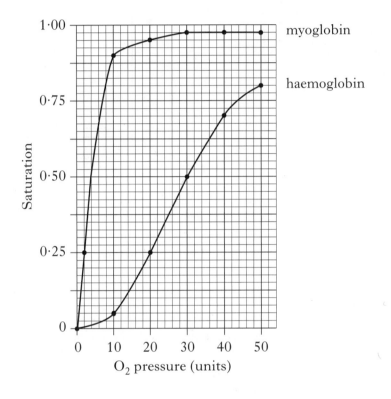

(a) (i) Use data to compare the saturation of myoglobin and haemoglobin between 0 and 30 units.   1

(ii) Explain how the information shows that quaternary structure affects the binding of oxygen to haemoglobin.   2

(b) Use the formula to calculate the change in the number of oxygen molecules bound to haemoglobin as the oxygen pressure is reduced from 30 to 20 units.   1

(c) Haem groups are an example of non-polypeptide components present in proteins. What term describes such components?   1

(5)

[Turn over

Marks

6. Gamma-aminobutyric acid (GABA) is a neurotransmitter that functions as a signalling molecule in the central nervous system. GABA binds to a receptor protein located in the plasma membrane of target cells as shown in Figure 1. Binding of a GABA molecule opens a channel that allows chloride ions (Cl⁻) to enter the cell.

Figure 1   **Figure 2**

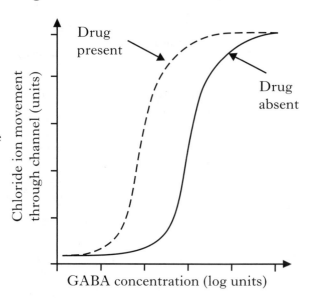

Benzodiazepines are sedative drugs that bind to the receptor protein and increase its affinity for GABA. These drugs act as allosteric modulators by binding at a site that is distinct from the GABA-binding site. Figure 2 above shows the movement of chloride ions through the channel as GABA is increased with and without the drug being present.

(a) (i)   State why neurotransmitters such as GABA cannot cross the membrane.   1

     (ii) What term describes the action of membrane receptors in which signal binding triggers an event in the cytoplasm that alters the behaviour of the cell?   1

(b) (i)   How does the information in Figure 2 show that the affinity of the receptor for GABA has been increased by the drug?   1

     (ii) How might the binding of benzodiazepine to the modulatory site increase the affinity of the receptor for GABA?   1

                                                                                    (4)

Marks

7. Cystic fibrosis is caused by mutation within the gene encoding the CFTR protein. The most common mutation in this gene is a three base-pair deletion that results in the loss of one amino acid from the CFTR protein. This deletion, $\Delta F508$, accounts for about 70% of mutations in cystic fibrosis.

   A screening test for cystic fibrosis uses the polymerase chain reaction (PCR) to amplify part of the *CFTR* gene containing the mutation.

   (a) Describe the features of primers used in PCR. 2

   (b) Give **one** technique that could be used in the detection of the mutation following PCR. 1

   (c) What information should be given to someone during counselling, following a negative screening result for $\Delta F508$? 1

   (4)

8. Answer **either** A **or** B.

   A. Compare prokaryotic and eukaryotic cells under the following headings:

       (i)   organisation of genetic material; 5

       (ii)   ultrastructure and other features. 10

   OR **(15)**

   B. Write notes on the cell cycle and its control under the following headings:

       (i)   interphase; 5

       (ii)   mitosis; 5

       (iii)   mutations. 5

   (15)

[END OF SECTION B]

[Turn over for Section C

SECTION C

Candidates should attempt questions on <u>one</u> unit, <u>either</u> Biotechnology <u>or</u> Animal Behaviour <u>or</u> Physiology, Health and Exercise.

The questions on Biotechnology can be found on pages 18–21.

The questions on Animal Behaviour can be found on pages 22–25.

The questions on Physiology, Health and Exercise can be found on pages 26–28.

All answers must be written clearly and legibly in ink.

Labelled diagrams may be used where appropriate.

BIOTECHNOLOGY   *Marks*

1.   The figure shows stages involved in the commercial production of an antibiotic.

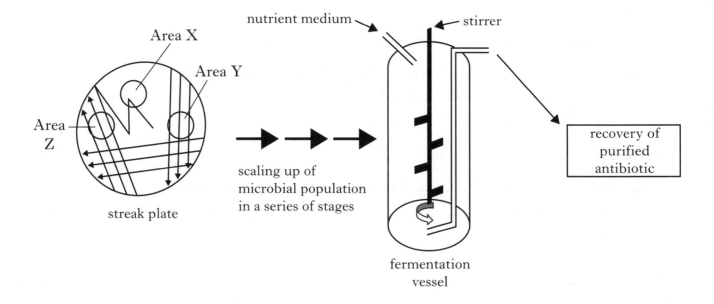

(a)   Name a commercially produced antibiotic and the type of micro-organism used in its production.   1

(b)   The scaling up process above is started using cells from a single isolated colony.

   (i)   Explain why it is necessary to use a single colony isolate.   1

   (ii)   Which one of the labelled areas on the streak plate would be most likely to have such a colony?   1

(c)   Give **one** reason why the culture in the fermentation vessel is stirred.   1

(d)   Give **one** process involved in the recovery of the antibiotic.   1

Marks

BIOTECHNOLOGY (continued)

1. (continued)

(e) The figure shows changes in the culture medium during the production of an antibiotic in a fermentation vessel.

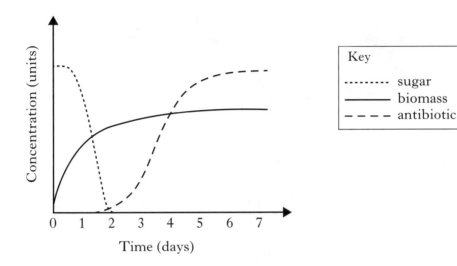

From the figure, give **two** pieces of evidence to indicate that this antibiotic is a secondary metabolite.

2

(7)

[Turn over

Marks

BIOTECHNOLOGY (continued)

2.   The diagram shows stages in the production of monoclonal antibodies.

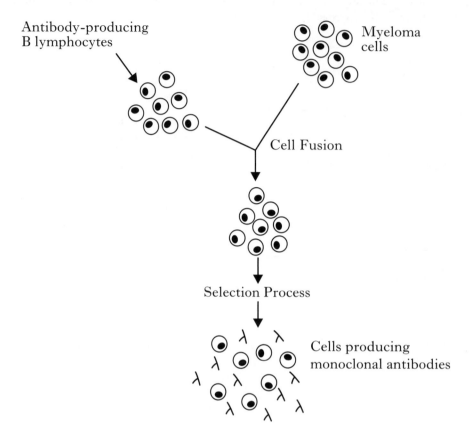

Antibody-producing
B lymphocytes

Myeloma
cells

Cell Fusion

Selection Process

Cells producing
monoclonal antibodies

(a)   Describe how the B lymphocytes shown above would have been produced.   2

(b)   Name the chemical used to bring about the fusion of B lymphocytes and myeloma
cells.   1

(c)   Give **one** use of monoclonal antibodies in the **treatment** of disease.   1

(4)

3.   The chemical composition of plant cell walls causes problems in the commercial
production of fruit juices. Identify the problems and outline how enzymes are used to
overcome them.   **(5)**

BIOTECHNOLOGY (continued)   *Marks*

4. Several studies have demonstrated the antimicrobial activity of oils extracted from plants. One such study investigated the bactericidal activity of an oil from cinnamon bark on the bacterium, methicillin-resistant *Staphylococcus aureus* (MRSA). The oil was added to broth containing an inoculum of MRSA.

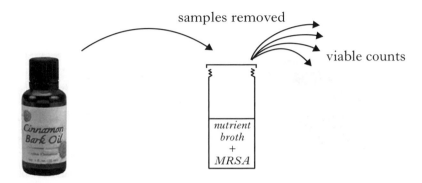

(a) Viable counts were made at intervals over a one hour period.

What is meant by a viable count?   **1**

(b) The graph below shows data for different concentrations of the cinnamon bark oil and a control with no oil. Log units are powers of ten.

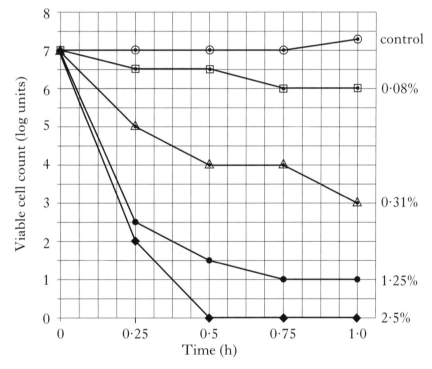

(i) In this study a bactericidal effect was defined as a reduction, over a one hour period, of 5 log units from the initial viable count.

Identify which of the oil treatments are bactericidal.   **1**

(ii) What aspect of the procedure was necessary to ensure that a valid comparison was made between the control and the treatments with essential oil?   **1**

(iii) By how many cells has the starting population been reduced in the 0·08% treatment after the first hour?   **1**

                                                                                 (4)

[End of *Biotechnology* questions. *Animal Behaviour* questions start on Page 22]

                                                                                 (20)

SECTION C (continued)

ANIMAL BEHAVIOUR

1. Northwestern crows (*Corvus caurinus*) can be observed feeding on the beaches of British Columbia in Canada. They search mainly for whelks (*Thais lamellosa*).

    Northwestern crow and whelk prey (not to scale)

    The crows search only for the largest whelks. After finding a whelk, they take off with it and fly vertically upwards before dropping it onto a rock. This is repeated until the whelk's shell is broken. Steep ascending flight of this kind is energetically expensive. The crows are very persistent and may drop a single whelk up to 20 times before the shell breaks.

    (a) The graph below shows the results of an experiment in which **researchers** dropped small, medium and large whelks from different heights. In the graph, "Total height" is obtained by combining the number of drops at each height required to break the whelk. The arrow on the X axis indicates the mean height of drop actually observed when **crows** drop whelks.

    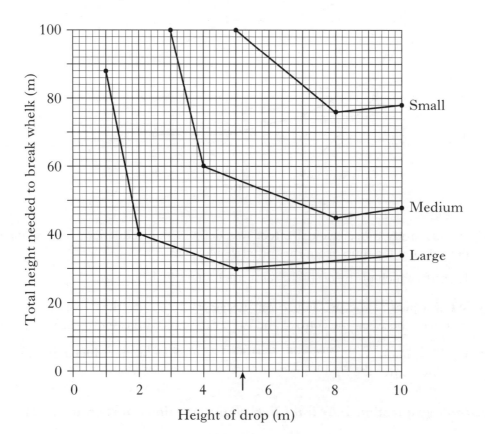

Marks

ANIMAL BEHAVIOUR (continued)

1. (a) (continued)

    (i) On average, how many times would a medium-sized whelk need to be dropped from a height of 4 m in order to break?   **1**

    (ii) From the information provided, suggest why crows take only the largest whelks.   **1**

  (b) Use the concept of optimal foraging to explain the observation that crows drop whelks from an average height of 5·2 m.   **2**

  (c) Apart from energy content and handling time, what other aspect of foraging behaviour is likely to be of significance in determining a predator's choice of prey?   **1**

        (5)

2. "All development depends on both nature and nurture." (R. Hinde)

  With reference to life span, compare the roles of nature and nurture in the behavioural development of adult invertebrates and primates.   **(5)**

[Turn over

Marks

ANIMAL BEHAVIOUR (continued)

3. The broad-nosed pipefish (*Syngnathus typhle*) can be found along many coasts and estuaries in the British Isles. In this species, "normal" sex roles are reversed: females compete with each other for males and it is the males that are selective. During mating, the female transfers her eggs into a brood pouch in the male where they are then fertilised and nourished. The males provide parental care for the young.

All pipefish are susceptible to infestation by a parasite that induces the formation of visible black spots on the skin.

Figure: Pipefish showing signs of parasite infestation

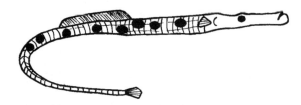

When females are infected, egg production decreases as the parasite load increases. High intensity infections may kill the fish host.

Experiments were carried out to discover male responses to spotted females that were either naturally infected or had been artificially tattooed using ink dissolved in a solvent. In both situations, it was found that males selected females with fewer or no black spots. Behavioural interactions between males, however, were not influenced by the presence or absence of spots on the males.

(a) During mating, the fish are more vulnerable to predators.

    (i) Explain how the male's preference for healthy females allows him to maximise his reproductive fitness.   2

    (ii) Explain why the genes controlling this behaviour might be described as "selfish".   1

(b) Give **one** aspect of behaviour that contributes to the high level of parental investment shown by the male pipefish.   1

(c) The parasite cannot be transmitted directly from one fish to another.

    Which aspect of pipefish behaviour is consistent with this observation?   1

(d) Suggest a control that should be used in the experiment involving tattooed spots.   1

(e) In the experiments, fish were arranged so that males could see females but females could not see males. Explain why this would strengthen the conclusion that males select against parasitised females using visual stimuli.   1

(7)

Marks

ANIMAL BEHAVIOUR (continued)

4. Cannibalism occurs when animals eat other animals of their own species. Willow leaf beetles, *Plagiodera versicolora*, lay eggs in clutches (groups). Females may have mated once or several times so clutches contain a mixture of half and full siblings. This means that the coefficient of relatedness, **r**, varies between 0·25 and 0·5.

   Larvae that hatch first eat unhatched eggs from the same clutch. 24 hours after hatching, cannibals are 30% heavier than non-cannibals.

   The scatterplot shows cannibalism rate and clutch relatedness for a number of populations.

   Figure: Cannibalism rate versus average clutch relatedness for each of eight populations

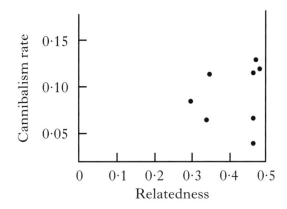

   (a) Why do full siblings have a coefficient of relatedness of 0·5?   1

   (b) A hypothesis from Hamilton's rule would be that cannibalistic larvae should not eat close relatives.

       (i)   What is meant by Hamilton's rule?   1

       (ii) What evidence from the graph contradicts the hypothesis?   1

                                                                                                          (3)

                                                                                                         (20)

[End of *Animal Behaviour* questions. *Physiology, Health and Exercise* questions start on Page 26]

[Turn over

SECTION C (continued)   *Marks*

PHYSIOLOGY, HEALTH AND EXERCISE

1. Describe how atherosclerosis can lead to myocardial infarction.   **(4)**

2. (*a*) To reduce the risk of cardiovascular disease, individuals are encouraged to improve the ratio of high-density lipoprotein (HDL) to low-density lipoprotein (LDL).

    Give **two** lifestyle factors that can be changed to improve the ratio of HDL:LDL.   **2**

    (*b*) Cholesterol in the blood is associated with HDL, LDL and triglycerides. Treatment with *statin* medication aims to improve the ratio of HDL to LDL by reducing cholesterol production.

    The data below show the blood lipid profiles of a patient before and after two years of statin medication, and the normal range of values for a healthy individual.

Blood lipid	Concentration (mmol/l)		
	Before treatment	*After treatment*	*Normal range values*
Total cholesterol	8·5	5·5	3·0 – 5·0
HDL	1·9	1·8	1·0 – 2·2
LDL	5·92	2·9	2·0 – 3·4
Triglycerides	1·5	1·7	0·3 – 2·5
Total cholesterol/HDL	4·5	3·1	about 3·0

    (i) LDL is not measured directly, it is calculated from other values using the formula below.

    LDL = (Total – HDL) – (Triglycerides / 2·2)

    Calculate the LDL value before treatment.   **1**

    (ii) Select **two** pieces of evidence to show that statin treatment has reduced the risk of cardiovascular disease.   **2**

    (iii) The aim for statin treatment is to increase the proportion of HDL to over 30% of the total. Use the data to show that this has been achieved.   **1**

                                                                                   (6)

Marks

PHYSIOLOGY, HEALTH AND EXERCISE (continued)

3. (*a*) Blood glucose concentration increases after a meal.

Describe the events that bring blood glucose concentration back to normal.   **2**

(*b*) In an *oral glucose tolerance test*, an individual has "impaired glucose tolerance" when results are in the range 7·8 to 11·0 mmol/l. A result in this range is referred to as *pre-diabetic*. If untreated, pre-diabetes leads to Type 2 diabetes (NIDDM).

The underlying cause of impaired glucose tolerance is insulin resistance.

(i) Explain why cells become less sensitive to insulin in individuals with insulin resistance.   **1**

(ii) For people with pre-diabetes, explain why there would be a long-term benefit from reducing a high waist to hip ratio.   **2**

(5)

[Turn over for Question 4 on *Page twenty-eight*

Marks

PHYSIOLOGY, HEALTH AND EXERCISE (continued)

4. (a) Why does taking part in sporting activities during adolescence reduce the risk of osteoporosis–related fractures in later life?

2

(b) The figure below shows the results of a study comparing bone mineral density of groups of women involved in different types of sport. The values show mean percentage difference in bone mineral density between the athletes and a control group who have an inactive lifestyle.

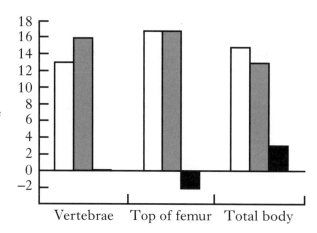

(i) Suggest why the study focuses on bone mineral density of vertebrae and the top of the femur (thigh).

1

(ii) Explain why swimmers are included in the study.

1

(iii) The data suggest that swimming has a negative effect on bone mineral density at the top of the femur. What other information would be required to judge if the results are statistically significant?

1

(5)

(20)

[END OF QUESTION PAPER]

ADVANCED HIGHER

2012

[BLANK PAGE]

X007/13/02

NATIONAL QUALIFICATIONS 2012	WEDNESDAY, 23 MAY 1.00 PM – 3.30 PM	BIOLOGY ADVANCED HIGHER

SECTION A—Questions 1–25 (25 marks)

Instructions for completion of Section A are given on *Page two*.

SECTIONS B AND C

The answer to each question should be written in ink in the answer book provided. Any additional paper (if used) should be placed inside the front cover of the answer book.

Rough work should be scored through.

Section B (55 marks)

All questions should be attempted. Candidates should note that Question 8 contains a choice.

Question 1 is on Pages 10, 11 and 12. Questions 2 and 3 are on Page 13. Pages 12 and 13 are fold-out pages.

Section C (20 marks)

Candidates should attempt the questions in **one** unit, **either** Biotechnology **or** Animal Behaviour **or** Physiology, Health and Exercise.

Read carefully

1　Check that the answer sheet provided is for **Biology Advanced Higher (Section A)**.

2　For this section of the examination you must use an **HB pencil** and, where necessary, an eraser.

3　Check that the answer sheet you have been given has **your name**, **date of birth**, **SCN** (Scottish Candidate Number) and **Centre Name** printed on it.

Do not change any of these details.

4　If any of this information is wrong, tell the Invigilator immediately.

5　If this information is correct, **print** your name and seat number in the boxes provided.

6　The answer to each question is **either** A, B, C or D. Decide what your answer is, then, using your pencil, put a horizontal line in the space provided (see sample question below).

7　There is **only one correct** answer to each question.

8　Any rough working should be done on the question paper or the rough working sheet, **not** on your answer sheet.

9　At the end of the examination, put the **answer sheet for Section A inside the front cover of the answer book**.

Sample Question

Which of the following molecules contains six carbon atoms?

A　Glucose

B　Pyruvic acid

C　Ribulose bisphosphate

D　Acetyl coenzyme A

The correct answer is **A**—Glucose. The answer **A** has been clearly marked in **pencil** with a horizontal line (see below).

Changing an answer

If you decide to change your answer, carefully erase your first answer and using your pencil, fill in the answer you want. The answer below has been changed to **D**.

SECTION A

All questions in this section should be attempted.

Answers should be given on the separate answer sheet provided.

1. Which line in the table below correctly represents the organelles in a prokaryotic cell?

	Chloroplast	Mitochondria	Ribosomes
A	Present	Absent	Absent
B	Absent	Absent	Present
C	Absent	Present	Absent
D	Present	Present	Present

2. The following diagram shows a bacterial cell.

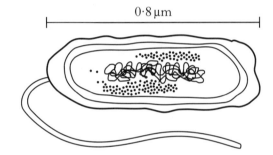

$0.8\,\mu m$

The length of this cell in millimetres (mm) is

A   800

B   80

C   0·008

D   0·0008.

3. In which of the following do both copies of the gene require a mutation for cancer to develop?

A   Oncogenes

B   Proto-oncogenes

C   Proliferation genes

D   Anti-proliferation genes

4. Which of the following is the correct sequence of stages in the production of plants by tissue culture? (PGR = plant growth regulators)

A   callus ⟶ explant $\xrightarrow{PGR}$ plantlet

B   explant $\xrightarrow{PGR}$ callus $\xrightarrow{PGR}$ plantlet

C   callus $\xrightarrow{PGR}$ explant $\xrightarrow{PGR}$ plantlet

D   explant ⟶ callus $\xrightarrow{PGR}$ plantlet

5. The key below can be used to identify carbohydrates.

1 ⎰ Sugars.. go to ...2
  ⎱ Polysaccharides .... go to ...4

2 ⎰ Monosaccharides.................................**A**
  ⎱ Disaccharides .... go to ...3

3 ⎰ Contains only one type of monomer .... **B**
  ⎱ Contains two types of monomer ....sucrose

4 ⎰ Storage function.......................... go to ...5
  ⎱ Structural function in plants ....**C**

5 ⎰ Storage function in animals......... glycogen
  ⎱ Storage function in plants ....**D**

Using the key, which letter would represent amylopectin?

[Turn over

6. Which of the diagrams below represents correctly a molecule of the steroid testosterone?

A

B

C

D

7. Which of the following is correct for a purine base?

	Ring structure	Example of base
A	double	adenine
B	double	thymine
C	single	adenine
D	single	thymine

8. A section of a double stranded DNA molecule contains 80 bases. 24 of these are thymine. The percentage of cytosine bases in the molecule is

A   12

B   16

C   20

D   30.

9. The diagram below shows a small polypeptide integrated into a membrane.

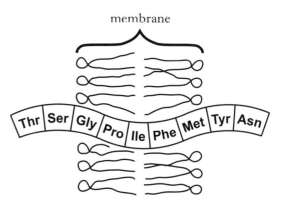

Which line in the table below correctly classifies amino acids in this polypeptide?

	Polar	Non-polar
A	Thr	Pro
B	Ile	Tyr
C	Asn	Ser
D	Phe	Gly

10. The mechanism of action of the sodium-potassium pump involves the following stages:

P   membrane protein is phosphorylated

Q   sodium ions bind to membrane protein

R   sodium ions are released

S   membrane protein changes conformation

The correct sequence is

A   P, Q, R, S

B   Q, P, S, R

C   Q, P, R, S

D   P, Q, S, R

11. The figure below shows how the ATPase activity of the sodium-potassium pump is affected by the concentrations of sodium and potassium ions.

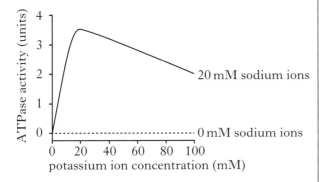

What valid conclusion can be drawn from this information?

A   The presence of potassium ions inhibits ATPase activity.

B   The optimal concentration of sodium ions for ATPase activity is 20 mM.

C   ATPase activity requires the presence of both sodium and potassium ions.

D   ATPase activity requires the presence of sodium ions only.

12. The DNA sequences of the normal and mutated versions of a gene are shown below.

Normal DNA sequence

GAGAATCCTTGAGCTCTTAAGCTTATT

Mutated DNA sequence

GAGAATCCTTGAGGTCTTAAGCTTATT

The table below gives the recognition sequences of four restriction endonucleases.

Restriction endonuclease	Recognition sequence
*Bam*H1	GGATCC
*Eco*R1	GAATTC
*Hind*III	AAGCTT
*Sac*I	GAGCTC

Which of the restriction endonucleases would produce different numbers of fragments when used to digest normal and mutant DNA?

A   *Bam*H1

B   *Eco*R1

C   *Hind*III

D   *Sac*I

13. During the production of transgenic tomato plants, plasmids can be used to transfer recombinant DNA from

A   *Rhizobium* to plant cell protoplasts

B   *Rhizobium* to differentiated plant cells

C   *Agrobacterium* to plant cell protoplasts

D   *Agrobacterium* to differentiated plant cells.

14. When a caterpillar consumes a plant leaf containing 200 kJ of energy, it passes 100 kJ of energy in its faeces, uses 67 kJ of energy for cellular respiration and uses 33 kJ of energy for new growth.

The amount of energy lost from the woodland ecosystem in this process is:

A   67 kJ

B   100 kJ

C   167 kJ

D   200 kJ

Questions 15 and 16 refer to the following diagram which shows the annual flow of energy through a terrestrial ecosystem. The units are kJ m^{-2}.

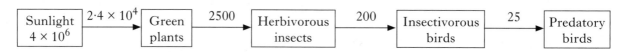

15. The organisms at trophic level 2 are

    A   producers

    B   primary consumers

    C   secondary consumers

    D   tertiary consumers.

16. Gross primary productivity (in kJ m^{-2}) for this ecosystem is

    A $2\cdot4 \times 10^4$

    B $2\cdot5 \times 10^3$

    C $4\cdot0 \times 10^6$

    D $21\cdot5 \times 10^3$.

17. The graph shows how productivity in a marsh was affected **after a time** by the experimental addition of nitrate and phosphate. Neither was added in the control experiment.

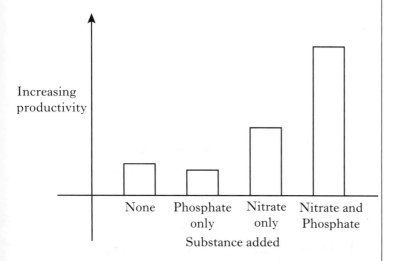

Which statement is supported by the graph?

    A   Productivity in the control is limited by both nitrate and phosphate.

    B   Phosphate can limit productivity if enough nitrate is available.

    C   Phosphate limits productivity in the control experiment.

    D   Productivity in the marsh is never limited by phosphate.

18. The pyramid below represents organisms in a food chain.

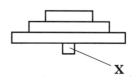

The part labelled **X** could represent

    A   phytoplankton in a pyramid of productivity

    B   oak trees in a pyramid of biomass

    C   phytoplankton in a pyramid of biomass

    D   oak trees in a pyramid of productivity.

19. Which of the following is an example of Batesian mimicry?

    A   Two harmful species of wasps that look like each other.

    B   A butterfly with large eyespots on its wings.

    C   A stick insect which looks like a twig.

    D   A harmless snake which resembles a poisonous species.

20. An experiment was carried out to investigate the density-dependent spread of a fungal disease of plants. Soil samples were taken near an infected plant. Half of the samples were sterilised.

The samples were then used to grow seedlings of the same species of plant at low or high density.

Which line in the table below would result in the highest percentage survival of the seedlings?

	Seedling density	Soil sterilised
A	low	no
B	high	no
C	low	yes
D	high	yes

21. The graphs below show how environmental changes can affect the internal conditions in aquatic organisms W, X, Y and Z.

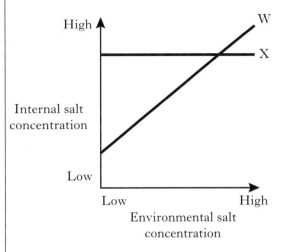

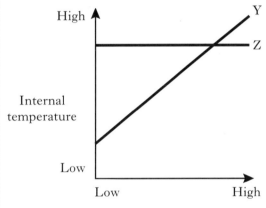

Which line in the table correctly identifies the osmoconformer and the homeotherm?

	Osmoconformer	Homeotherm
A	W	Y
B	W	Z
C	X	Y
D	X	Z

[Turn over

22. The table below shows information about plants in fenced and unfenced grassland plots after 2 years. The plots were fenced to exclude voles which feed mainly on annual grasses.

	Relative biomass (units)		Number of plant species	
	Fenced plots	Unfenced plots	Fenced plots	Unfenced plots
Annual grasses	120	40	6	6
Other plants	40	80	12	24

Which line of the table below best summarises the effects of grazing on the grassland?

	Plant growth (biomass units)	Plant diversity (number of species)
A	increased	increased
B	increased	decreased
C	decreased	decreased
D	decreased	increased

23. Which of the following does **not** result in loss of complexity in ecosystems?

A   Predation

B   Monoculture

C   Eutrophication

D   Toxic pollution

24. Bleaching of coral occurs because

A   pollution prevents them producing coloured pigments

B   toxic chemicals kill zooxanthellae in the corals

C   their symbiotic partners are sensitive to increasing temperature

D   zooxanthellae in the corals are sensitive to UV light.

25. Allogenic succession takes place

A   as a result of climatic change

B   after clearing of agricultural land

C   when more sand is deposited on a beach

D   during decomposition.

[END OF SECTION A]

Candidates are reminded that the answer sheet MUST be returned INSIDE the front cover of the answer book.

[Turn over for Section B on *Page ten*

SECTION B

All questions in this section should be attempted.

All answers must be written clearly and legibly in ink.

1. Recently a new class of RNA, called **micro**RNA, has been discovered. These small RNA molecules have an important role in controlling the translation of mRNA. This type of control is called *RNA interference*.

   A microRNA is formed from a *precursor* RNA molecule that folds into a double-stranded "hairpin" structure. The hairpin is then processed to give a shorter molecule by the enzymes "Drosha" and "Dicer". One strand of this short molecule attaches to RISC proteins; the resulting complex binds to target mRNA molecules and prevents translation. (Figure 1)

   Figure 1: Control of gene expression by RNA interference

   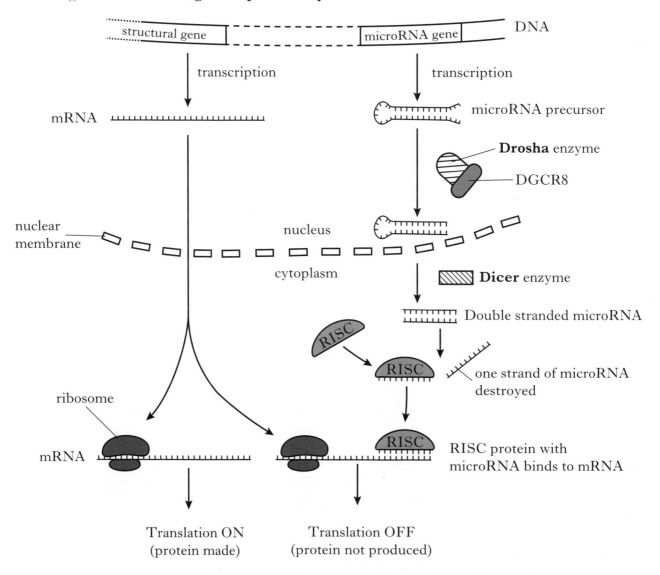

   Recent research has investigated the importance of microRNA in controlling the fate of stem cells. Stem cells can either divide rapidly to make more stem cells, a process called **self-renewal**, or differentiate into specialised cell types. To determine the role of microRNAs in these processes, stem cells were modified to "knock out" microRNA production. These microRNA *knockout cells* lack the protein DGCR8, an activator of Drosha. Figures 2A and 2B compare growth rate and cell-cycle progression in knockout and normal cells.

Question 1 (continued)

In further work, the differentiation of knockout and normal cells was studied by inducing the cells to differentiate. Analysis was carried out on the levels of specific marker molecules whose presence is associated with either self-renewal or differentiation. Results are shown in Figures 3A and 3B.

Figure 2A: Effect of knockout on growth rate

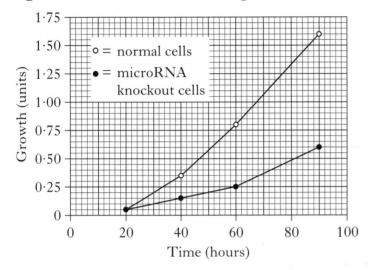

Figure 2B: Effect of knockout on cell cycle

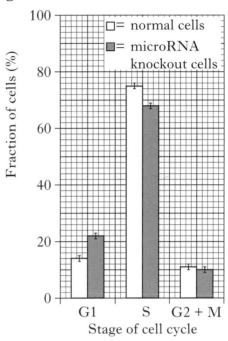

Figure 3A: Level of self-renewal marker

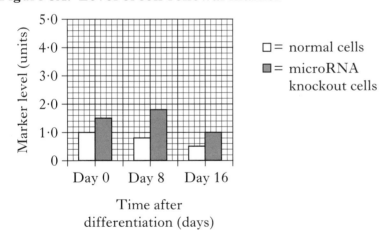

Figure 3B: Level of differentiation marker

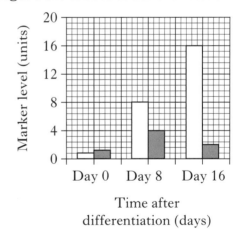

[Question 1 continues on *Page twelve*

Marks

Question 1 (continued)

(a) During the formation of microRNAs, single-stranded RNA molecules form hairpin structures as shown in the diagram below.

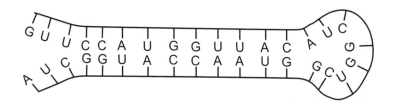

    (i) Which covalent bonds join nucleotides in RNA molecules? 1

    (ii) What is the role of hydrogen bonding in maintaining the hairpin shape? 1

(b) Describe how the knockout of DGCR8 affects RNA interference. 2

(c) (i) Refer to Figure 2A. Calculate the percentage reduction in growth at 90 hours caused by the microRNA knockout. 1

    (ii) The authors concluded that microRNA knockout cells do not progress normally through the cell cycle. How do the results in Figure 2B support this conclusion? 2

(d) Refer to Figures 3A and 3B.

    (i) Comparing normal and knockout cells, give **two** general conclusions about the expression of the differentiation marker. 2

    (ii) What evidence is there that self-renewal is switched off as differentiation proceeds and that the interaction of these two processes is abnormal in knockout cells? 2

(e) MicroRNAs inhibit *translation*. Describe how the *transcription* of β-galactosidase in prokaryotes is switched off. 2

(13)

[Questions 2 and 3 are on fold-out *Page thirteen*

Marks

2. Some fish species can change the colour of their skin by moving pigment granules within skin cells. The granules are attached to microtubules and can either aggregate in the centre of the cell or disperse throughout the cytoplasm.

    Movement of granules along microtubules is controlled by hydrophilic signalling molecules that alter the concentration of the intracellular signalling molecule cyclic AMP (cAMP).

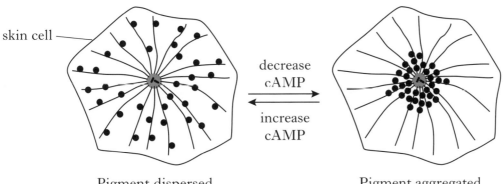

decrease cAMP

increase cAMP

Pigment dispersed   Pigment aggregated

   (a) (i) Explain why the control of pigment movement by hormones is an example of signal transduction.   2

   (ii) Suggest how the movement of pigments to alter skin colour could function in defence against predation.   1

   (b) (i) Microtubules have a role in governing the location of cell components. Give **one** other function of the cytoskeleton.   1

   (ii) Name the protein component of microtubules.   1

   (iii) From which structure do microtubules radiate?   1

            (6)

3. Describe the control of enzyme activity by competitive and non-competitive inhibitors.   **(5)**

Marks

4. Duchenne muscular dystrophy (DMD) is an inherited condition resulting from a deletion mutation within the dystrophin gene of the X-chromosome.

A sample of DNA from an individual (P) suspected of having DMD was isolated and digested with a restriction endonuclease. A corresponding control sample (C) was treated in the same way. The resulting fragments were separated using gel electrophoresis. The outcome is shown in the diagram below.

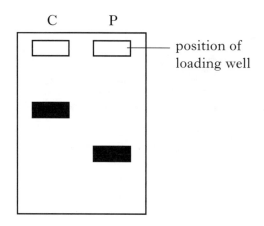

(a) How are specific gene fragments identified in this procedure?   1

(b) State whether or not the results confirm a diagnosis of DMD and explain your answer.   2

(c) An alternative method of genetic screening for DMD involves the amplification of regions of the dystrophin gene. Name the technique used to amplify DNA.   1

(4)

Marks

5. The gannet (*Morus bassanus*) is a fish-eating seabird that breeds on barren, rocky offshore islands in the North Atlantic. A study from 1963 to 1976 investigated the negative impact of DDE on gannet breeding success. DDE, a residue from DDT breakdown, causes thinning of egg shells.

(a) What term is used to describe the increase in DDE concentration shown in the table below?

1

Gannet age class	DDE concentration in muscle tissue (ppm)
1 year	0·08
2 years	0·50
3–4 years	0·96
Adult	2·17

(b) The table below shows aspects of breeding success in two different island colonies.

Island colony	Egg hatching success (%)	Chick survival (%)
Ailsa Craig, Scotland	81	92
Bonaventure, Canada	38	78

(i) At Ailsa Craig, 75% of eggs laid resulted in the survival of a chick.

Use the data to calculate the corresponding survival rate for eggs laid at Bonaventure.

1

(ii) DDT was sprayed to protect hillside forests in mainland Canada from severe caterpillar outbreaks.

Explain how the pollutant came to be present in the gannets at Bonaventure.

2

(4)

[Turn over

Marks

6. The Antarctic krill (*Euphausia superba*) is the major primary consumer in the marine food web of the Southern Ocean. They feed on algae, the producers. The ecological efficiency of krill is low.

Antarctic krill

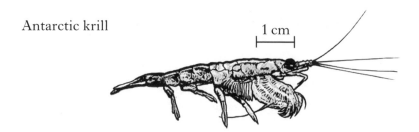

1 cm

(a) Ecological efficiency is the energy in one trophic level as a percentage of energy in the level below. Give **one** reason for a low ecological efficiency.

1

(b) Young krill scrape algae from below the ice sheets that form during winter. Once the ice melts, the krill must feed on algae in open water. At this time, they become the main food source of many Antarctic species including penguins, seals and whales.

Long-term studies have monitored krill density in relation to winter ice duration.

The results below suggest that as winter ice duration increases the population density of krill increases.

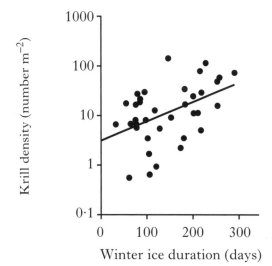

(i) Suggest an explanation for the trend shown in the graph.

1

(ii) Krill have the highest total biomass of any species of animal. Their faeces fall to the deep ocean floor where decomposition rates are so low that there is no significant recycling of carbon dioxide back to the atmosphere.

With reference to krill faeces, explain how a rise in sea temperature in Antarctica caused by global warming could lead to a further increase in global warming.

2

(4)

Marks

7. The rose-grain aphid (*Metopolophium dirhodum*) is a herbivorous insect that requires two different types of plant to complete its lifecycle. It spends the winter as an egg in diapause on wild roses found in hedgerows. In spring, its numbers build up and it migrates to feed on nearby wheat crops. The rose-grain aphid is an important vector for major plant viruses that reduce grain yields.

   (*a*) What is meant by the term diapause? **1**

   (*b*) Suggest why the increased field sizes associated with intensive wheat cultivation may help to reduce crop losses due to rose-grain aphid outbreaks. **2**

   (*c*) What is meant by the biological term "vector"? **1**

   (4)

8. Answer **either** A **or** B.

   A. Write notes on niche and competition. Use examples as appropriate. **(15)**

   OR

   B. Give an account of the circulation of nutrients under the following headings:

   (i) decomposition;

   (ii) nutrient cycling. **(15)**

[END OF SECTION B]

[Turn over for Section C

SECTION C

Candidates should attempt questions on <u>one</u> unit, <u>either</u> Biotechnology <u>or</u> Animal Behaviour <u>or</u> Physiology, Health and Exercise.

The questions on Biotechnology can be found on pages 18–21.

The questions on Animal Behaviour can be found on pages 22–25.

The questions on Physiology, Health and Exercise can be found on pages 26–28.

All answers must be written clearly and legibly in ink.

Labelled diagrams may be used where appropriate.

BIOTECHNOLOGY

1.   The diagram shows stages in the production of a monoclonal antibody.

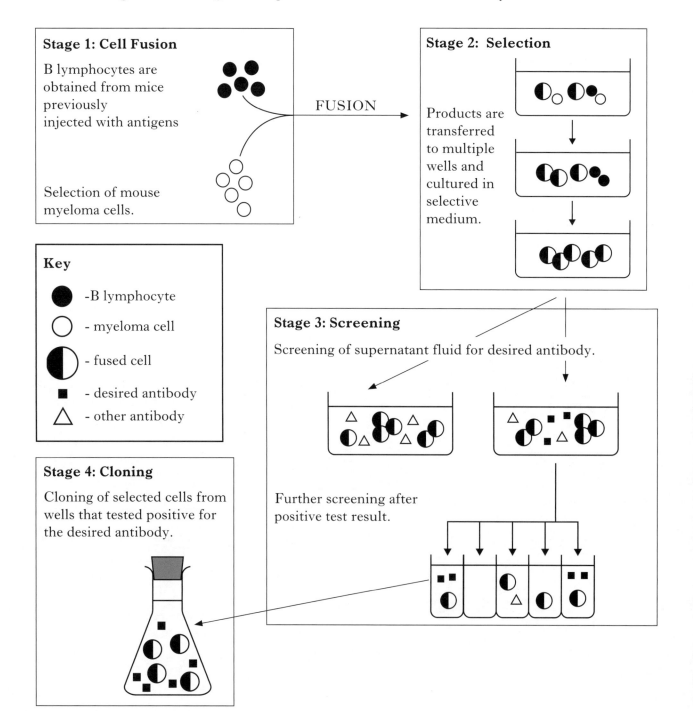

Marks

BIOTECHNOLOGY (continued)

1. **(continued)**

   (*a*) Which organ in the mouse is used as a source of B lymphocytes?   **1**

   (*b*) Why are the mouse B lymphocytes fused with myeloma cells?   **1**

   (*c*) Refer to Stage 2 on the diagram.

       (i) Explain why unfused myeloma cells do not progress to Stage 3.   **1**

       (ii) Explain why B lymphocytes do not progress to Stage 3.   **1**

   (*d*) With reference to Stage 3, explain the need for screening to occur in two steps.   **2**

       (6)

2. Describe how the *growth rate constant* of a bacterial culture can be determined.

   What is its relevance when culturing bacteria for enzyme production?   **(5)**

[Turn over

Marks

BIOTECHNOLOGY (continued)

3. (a) Various enzymes are used in fruit juice production.

      (i) Name an enzyme used to decrease viscosity during extraction.   **1**

      (ii) Why might arabanase be added to the extracted product?   **1**

(b) The diagram illustrates a technique used to purify an enzyme secreted by a culture of microbial cells in a fermenter.

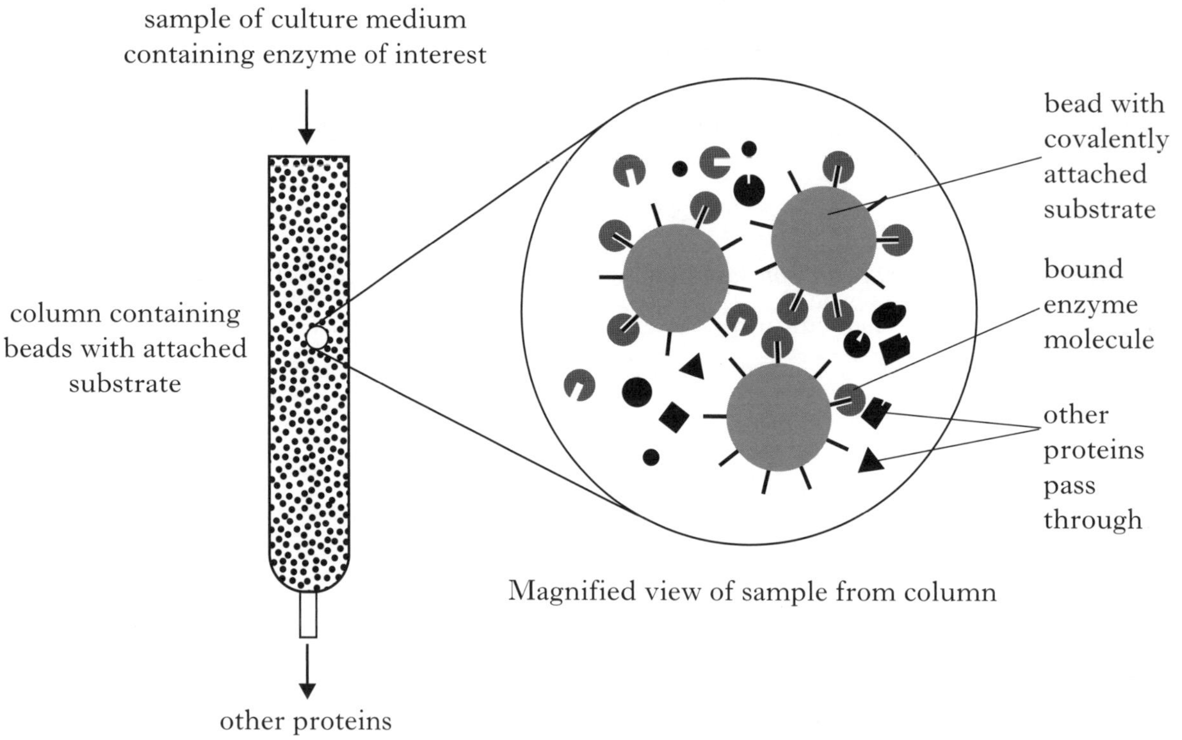

Magnified view of sample from column

      (i) What general term is given to the purification technique shown above?   **1**

      (ii) What feature of the enzyme molecule allows it to be separated from the other proteins as the sample passes through the column?   **1**

                                                                       (4)

Marks

BIOTECHNOLOGY (continued)

4. To make yoghurt, milk is pasteurised and then inoculated with bacteria that allow fermentation to occur. Two species commonly used together in the inoculum are *Lactobacillus bulgaricus* and *Streptococcus thermophilus*.

    (a) What is the purpose of pasteurisation?   1

    (b) The fermentation is a two-stage process.

        (i) State the chemical conversion taking place in the first stage.   1

        (ii) What is the role of the second stage?   1

    (c) The graph shows the growth of *L. bulgaricus* and *S. thermophilus* in both pure and mixed culture.

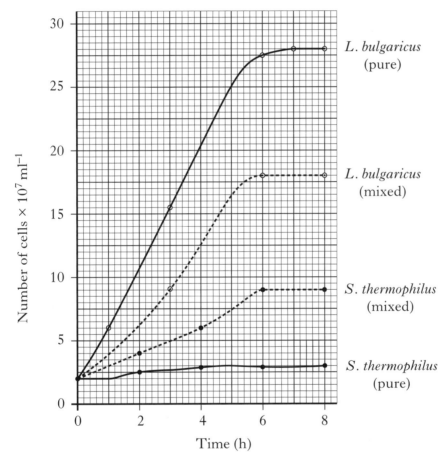

        (i) Calculate the reduction in growth of *L. bulgaricus* at 8 hours as a result of being in the mixed culture.   1

        (ii) Scientists have suggested that *S. thermophilus* receives a growth promoting substance in this mixed culture. How do the data support that conclusion?   1

(5)

[End of *Biotechnology* questions. *Animal Behaviour* questions start on Page 22]

Marks

SECTION C (continued)

ANIMAL BEHAVIOUR

1. The proportion of time that individual prey animals spend being vigilant may be affected by both the risk of predation and group size. Kudu (Figure 1) are a frequent prey of lions, with most attacks occurring by ambush within two kilometres of water holes. The vigilance behaviour of kudu at water holes has been studied in Hwange National Park, Zimbabwe.

Figure 1: Kudu

Figure 2: Effect of presence of lions and kudu group size on vigilance

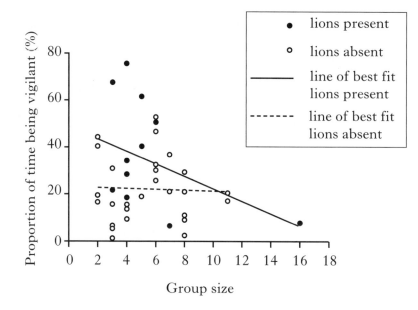

(a) Describe what vigilance behaviour would look like in an animal such as a kudu.   1

(b) Figure 2 shows the proportion of time individual kudu spend being vigilant during drinking, when in different group sizes and when lions are present or absent.

   (i) Suggest **one** strategy that should be used in the observation and recording of kudu vigilance behaviour.   1

   (ii) The researchers hypothesised that individual vigilance would decrease as group size increased, and increase in the presence of lions.

      Use the results to evaluate these hypotheses.   2

   (iii) Comment on the reliability of the data recorded when lions were present.   1

(5)

Marks

ANIMAL BEHAVIOUR (continued)

2. Figure 1 shows the cichlid fish *Cyathopharynx furcifer* found in Lake Tanganyika in Africa. Sexually active males build the sandy substrate into crater-like structures (mating craters). The male fish display around these spawning sites with intense colour. The crater itself has no role in the rearing of the brood produced after fertilisation. Figure 2 shows the results of an investigation into male body size and crater diameter.

Figure 1: Male cichlid in mating crater   Figure 2: Male body size and crater diameter

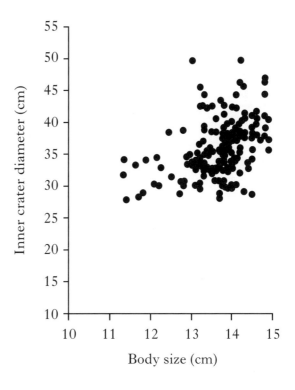

(a) Describe the relationship between body size and crater size shown in Figure 2.   1

(b) When crater sizes were either enlarged or reduced by researchers, within a day the males rebuilt the craters to their original sizes, even the enlarged ones.

   (i) Explain why the researchers concluded that mating craters in *C. furcifer* are extended phenotypes.   1

   (ii) Give another example of an extended phenotype in a species.   1

(c) State **one** feature of a male cichlid that is likely to have evolved as a result of sexual selection.   1

                                                (4)

[Turn over

ANIMAL BEHAVIOUR (continued)

3. Meerkats (*Suricata suricatta*) are social mammals living in the Kalahari Desert. They show co-operative breeding in which a dominant male and dominant female monopolise reproduction. Subordinate animals rarely reproduce but help to rear the offspring of the dominant pair. They are not necessarily closely related to the young animals that they help to rear.

Figure 1: Meerkats

As in the dominance hierarchies of many primate groups, grooming behaviour can be frequently observed in meerkats. Figure 2 shows the frequency of grooming between dominant females and young, subordinate animals.

Figure 2: Grooming of juveniles by dominant females

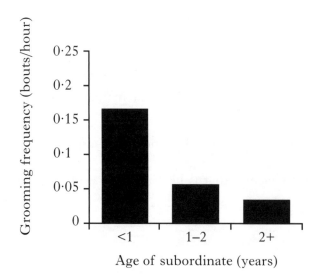

Marks

ANIMAL BEHAVIOUR (continued)

3. (continued)

   (a) (i) Use Figure 2 to support the hypothesis that one function of meerkat grooming is concerned with parental care. **1**

   (ii) State an aspect of grooming behaviour, other than frequency, that could be observed and recorded. **1**

   (b) State **two** other functions of grooming in social mammals such as primates. **2**

   (c) Select a statement from the information given about meerkats that may seem to be at odds with the concept of the "selfish" gene. Justify your answer. **2**

   (6)

4. Discuss the characteristics of sign stimuli and fixed action patterns. How do they interact in the feeding of young birds by their parents? **(5)**

[End of *Animal Behaviour* questions. *Physiology, Health and Exercise* questions start on Page 26]

[Turn over

Marks

SECTION C (continued)

PHYSIOLOGY, HEALTH AND EXERCISE

1. In the cardiac cycle, ventricles contract and force blood into the arteries during systole; during diastole the chambers are relaxed and the ventricles fill with blood.

   (a) What do the values 120/70 represent in a normal blood pressure reading?　1

   (b) Explain how plaque formation in artery walls can lead to raised blood pressure.　2

   (c) The most widespread cardiovascular disease in western countries is atherosclerosis in coronary arteries. The most common symptom is angina pectoris, chest pain that develops from oxygen shortage in the myocardial circulation during exertion.

   Oxygen is delivered to heart muscle during diastole as ventricles relax. When heart rate changes, the durations of systole and diastole change, as shown in the table below.

Heart rate (bpm)	Duration of systole (s)	Duration of diastole (s)
65	0·27	0·65
75	0·27	0·53
200	0·16	0·14

   (i) Calculate the % decrease in duration of systole when heart rate increases from 65 to 200 bpm.　1

   (ii) Use information provided to explain why, in individuals with atherosclerosis, exertion can cause angina.　2

   (d) Most of the treatments to relieve angina aim to dilate the coronary arteries. However, a relatively new drug, *ivabradine*, has been successful in the treatment of angina by only reducing heart rate.

Marks

PHYSIOLOGY, HEALTH AND EXERCISE (continued)

1. (*d*) (continued)

The figure below shows the effect of exercise tolerance tests on angina patients, exercised until the onset of chest pain. Patients were given tablets containing a dose of *ivabradine* or a placebo (where the tablet contained no drug). The change in response is calculated from each individual's result before and after taking the tablets.

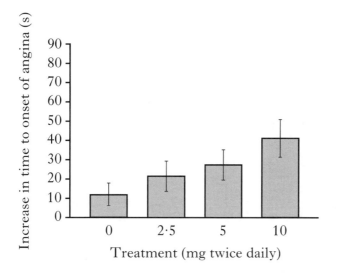

What evidence is there that the medication is effective?   1

(7)

2. Obesity is defined as a body mass index (BMI) greater than 30 (kg/m^2). BMI is not a measure of body composition. Other methods are used to determine percentage body fat, such as densitometry and bioelectrical impedance analysis.

   (*a*) Is an individual with a height of 1·82 m and mass of 90 kg obese?

   Justify your answer.   1

   (*b*) (i) What **two** measurements are required in densitometry?   1

   (ii) How is the density value used to obtain percentage body fat?   1

   (*c*) What is the drawback of using bioelectrical impedance analysis with obese individuals?   1

(4)

[Turn over

Marks

PHYSIOLOGY, HEALTH AND EXERCISE (continued)

3. Medical scientists are increasingly focusing research on *"metabolic syndrome"*, a group of risk factors that apply to both Type 2 diabetes (NIDDM) and cardiovascular diseases. Risk factors include increased insulin concentrations, increased fasting glucose, increased blood triglycerides and decreased HDL. The underlying concern is their common link to *insulin resistance*, a loss of sensitivity to insulin.

   (a) What effect does exercise have on the lipid profile of blood?   **1**

   (b) Explain how exercise reduces blood glucose in Type 2 diabetes.   **2**

   (c) In an investigation, volunteers with metabolic syndrome were monitored following different periods of jogging on a treadmill at 60% of their VO_{2max}. They fasted for 12 hours after the exercise period then consumed a high-energy drink and remained at rest. Blood samples were taken following the high-energy drink and at two-hour intervals. Results for insulin concentration are shown below.

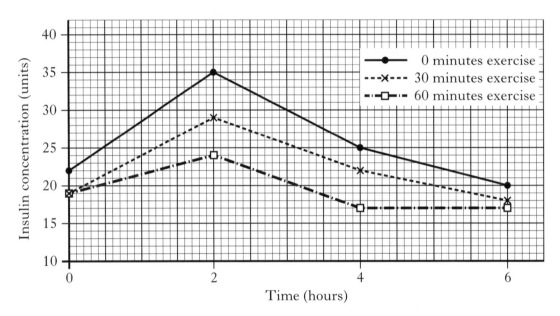

   Give **one** conclusion that can be drawn from the experiment about the possible role of exercise in the control of metabolic syndrome. Use data to support your answer.   **2**

   (5)

4. Discuss the contribution of exercise to a weight-control programme.   **(4)**

[END OF QUESTION PAPER]

ADVANCED HIGHER

2013

[BLANK PAGE]

X007/13/02

NATIONAL QUALIFICATIONS 2013	WEDNESDAY, 15 MAY 1.00 PM – 3.30 PM	BIOLOGY ADVANCED HIGHER

SECTION A—Questions 1–25 (25 marks)

Instructions for completion of Section A are given on *Page two*.

SECTIONS B AND C

The answer to each question should be written in ink in the answer book provided. Any additional paper (if used) should be placed inside the front cover of the answer book.

Rough work should be scored through.

Section B (55 marks)

All questions should be attempted. Candidates should note that Question 8 contains a choice.

Question 1 is on Pages 10, 11 and 12. Question 2 is on Page 12 and Question 3 is on Page 13. Pages 12 and 13 are fold-out pages.

Section C (20 marks)

Candidates should attempt the questions in **one** unit, **either** Biotechnology **or** Animal Behaviour **or** Physiology, Health and Exercise.

Read carefully

1   Check that the answer sheet provided is for **Biology Advanced Higher (Section A)**.

2   For this section of the examination you must use an **HB pencil** and, where necessary, an eraser.

3   Check that the answer sheet you have been given has **your name**, **date of birth**, **SCN** (Scottish Candidate Number) and **Centre Name** printed on it.

    Do not change any of these details.

4   If any of this information is wrong, tell the Invigilator immediately.

5   If this information is correct, **print** your name and seat number in the boxes provided.

6   The answer to each question is **either** A, B, C or D. Decide what your answer is, then, using your pencil, put a horizontal line in the space provided (see sample question below).

7   There is **only one correct** answer to each question.

8   Any rough working should be done on the question paper or the rough working sheet, **not** on your answer sheet.

9   At the end of the examination, put the **answer sheet for Section A inside the front cover of the answer book**.

Sample Question

Which of the following molecules contains six carbon atoms?

A   Glucose

B   Pyruvic acid

C   Ribulose bisphosphate

D   Acetyl coenzyme A

The correct answer is **A**—Glucose. The answer **A** has been clearly marked in **pencil** with a horizontal line (see below).

Changing an answer

If you decide to change your answer, carefully erase your first answer and using your pencil, fill in the answer you want. The answer below has been changed to **D**.

A   B   C   D

SECTION A

All questions in this section should be attempted.

Answers should be given on the separate answer sheet provided.

1. Which of the following structures is present in both eukaryotic and prokaryotic cells?

   A   Ribosomes

   B   Mitochondria

   C   Pili

   D   Centrioles

2. The figure below shows the number of cells in a tissue sample at various stages of the cell cycle.

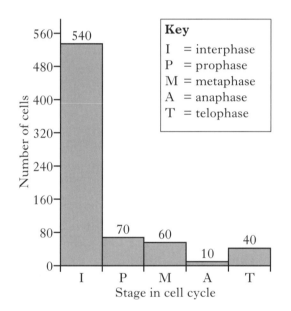

Key
I = interphase
P = prophase
M = metaphase
A = anaphase
T = telophase

The mitotic index for this sample is

   A   3

   B   4

   C   25

   D   33.

3. Which of the following genes encodes proteins that prevent the development of tumours by restricting cell division?

   A   Oncogenes

   B   Regulator genes

   C   Proto-oncogenes

   D   Anti-proliferation genes

4. Which line in the table correctly describes the chemical reaction in which two monosaccharides are joined together?

	Type of reaction	Type of bond formed
A	hydrolysis	glycosidic
B	condensation	glycosidic
C	hydrolysis	ester
D	condensation	ester

5. An unbranched polysaccharide is made up of glucose monomers joined together by $\beta(1-4)$ linkages. This polysaccharide could be

   A   amylopectin

   B   cellulose

   C   amylose

   D   glycogen.

6. Which of the following statements about the sodium-potassium pump is correct?

   A   The transport protein has an affinity for sodium ions in the cytoplasm.

   B   It results in a higher concentration of sodium ions inside the cell.

   C   The transport protein has an affinity for sodium ions in the extracellular fluid.

   D   It results in a higher concentration of potassium ions outside the cell.

7. The total surface area of a red blood cell is about $136 \, \mu m^2$. A single sodium-potassium ATPase molecule takes up an area of $1 \times 10^{-4} \, \mu m^2$. In total these molecules account for 0·5% of the cell surface area.

   Approximately how many of these molecules are there on the surface of one red blood cell?

   A   13 600

   B   6 800

   C   3 400

   D   680

8. Which of the following describes the structure of thymine?

A   A pyrimidine base with a single-ring structure.

B   A pyrimidine base with a double-ring structure.

C   A purine base with a single-ring structure.

D   A purine base with a double-ring structure.

9. The role of the polymerase chain reaction (PCR) is to

A   profile DNA

B   anneal DNA

C   replicate DNA

D   sequence DNA.

10. A short stretch of a DNA molecule that could be used as a template for the polymerase chain reaction (PCR) is shown below.

5' ATTCCGGTCGACCGGTAC 3'

top strand

3' TAAGGCCAGCTGGCCATG 5'

bottom strand

Which of the following correctly represents the base sequence of a primer that would bind to the **top** strand of the template DNA?

A   5' TGGCCTTA 3'

B   5' ATTCCGGT 3'

C   5' ACCGGAAT 3'

D   5' TAAGGCCA 3'

11. Enzymes that catalyse the hydrolysis of phosphodiester bonds in genetic material are called

A   ligases

B   kinases

C   nucleases

D   polymerases.

12. The graph below shows the mass of product resulting from an enzyme controlled reaction.

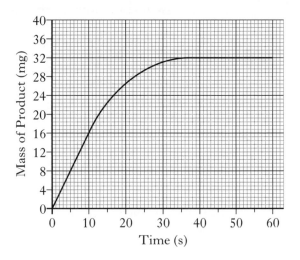

What is the initial rate of reaction?

A $0.53 \, \text{mg s}^{-1}$

B $0.63 \, \text{mg s}^{-1}$

C $0.89 \, \text{mg s}^{-1}$

D $1.60 \, \text{mg s}^{-1}$

13. A marine food chain is shown below.

phytoplankton ⟶ zooplankton ⟶ fish

The phytoplankton have a lower biomass than the zooplankton. The food chain will remain stable if

A   other consumers eat the phytoplankton

B   there are larger numbers of phytoplankton than zooplankton

C   the fish also feed on other producers

D   the phytoplankton have a higher productivity than the zooplankton.

14. The table below shows the areas of four aquatic ecosystems and their contribution to world net primary production.

Ecosystem number	Description	Area (millions km^2)	World net primary production (10^9 tonnes/year)
1	Estuaries	1·4	2·1
2	Upwelling zones	0·4	0·2
3	Lakes and streams	2·0	0·5
4	Continental shelf	26·6	9·6

The order of increasing net primary productivity for these ecosystems is

A   3 → 4 → 2 → 1

B   3 → 2 → 1 → 4

C   4 → 2 → 1 → 3

D   1 → 2 → 4 → 3.

15. The decomposition of leaf litter on the floor of a tropical rainforest was studied monthly over a year. The changes in some abiotic factors were also recorded. The graphs below show the results.

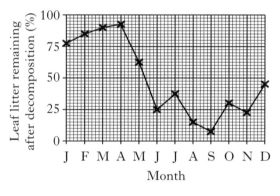

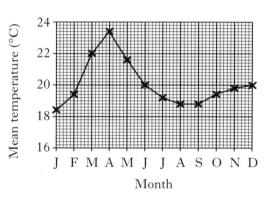

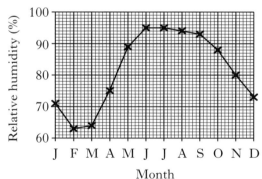

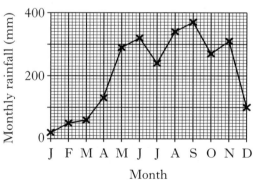

Which row in the table below correctly identifies changes in abiotic factors that **increase** the rate of decomposition?

	Mean temperature	Relative humidity	Monthly rainfall
A	Higher	Lower	Lower
B	Lower	Higher	Higher
C	Higher	Lower	Higher
D	Lower	Higher	Lower

16. Which line in the table identifies correctly micro-organisms responsible for nitrogen fixation and for nitrification in the soil?

	Micro-organisms	
	Nitrogen fixation	*Nitrification*
A	*Rhizobium*	Cyanobacteria
B	*Nitrobacter*	*Nitrosomonas*
C	*Nitrosomonas*	*Rhizobium*
D	Cyanobacteria	*Nitrobacter*

17. A flask containing some soil in a solution of ammonium salts was set up to demonstrate the activity of nitrifying bacteria. The concentrations of ammonium, nitrite and nitrate ions were measured over several weeks and the results are shown in the following graph.

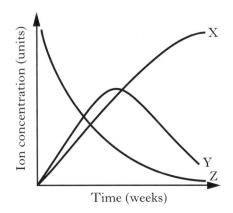

Which line in the table below correctly represents the results obtained?

	X	*Y*	*Z*
A	nitrate	nitrite	ammonium
B	nitrite	nitrate	ammonium
C	ammonium	nitrite	nitrate
D	nitrate	ammonium	nitrite

18. The information below shows the distribution of beak sizes in two species of finches living separately and living together.

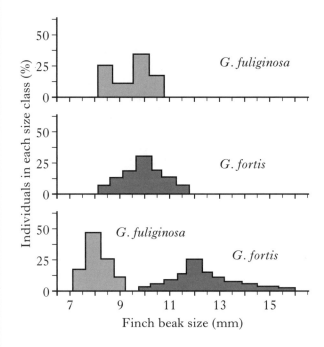

The changes in distribution are a result of

A   intraspecific competition

B   competitive exclusion

C   resource partitioning

D   exploitation competition.

19. The graph below shows the relationship between the number of breeding pairs in a songbird population and the mean clutch size (number of eggs in a nest).

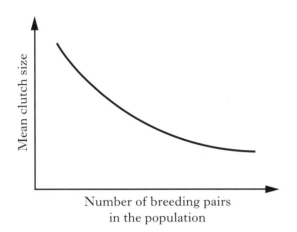

The graph shows that clutch size is affected by

A   intraspecific competition that is density dependent

B   intraspecific competition that is density independent

C   interspecific competition that is density dependent

D   interspecific competition that is density independent.

20. The gases shown in the table below may contribute to acid rain (AR) and the greenhouse effect (GE). Which line in the table correctly shows the contribution of each gas?

	Gas					
	CFC		Carbon dioxide		Methane	
	AR	GE	AR	GE	AR	GE
A	✓	✗	✓	✓	✗	✓
B	✗	✓	✗	✓	✓	✗
C	✓	✓	✓	✗	✓	✓
D	✗	✓	✓	✓	✗	✓

21. Coral bleaching is the result of an increase in

A   ultraviolet radiation

B   nutrient concentration

C   seawater temperature

D   populations of zooxanthellae.

22. The following formula can be used to estimate population size from mark and recapture data.

$$N = MC/R$$

Where N = population estimate
   M = number first captured, marked and released
   C = total number in second capture
   R = number marked in second capture

In a survey to estimate a peppered moth population, the following data were obtained:

Moths captured, marked and released = 200
Marked moths in second capture   = 60
Unmarked moths in second capture   = 240

The estimated population of the moths was

A   500

B   600

C   800

D   1000.

[Turn over

23. For a species of butterfly, the duration of its flight periods and the week of its first sighting were recorded from 1976 to 1998.

Graph 1: Duration of flight period

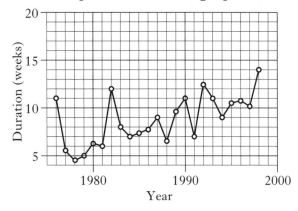

Graph 2: Week of first sighting

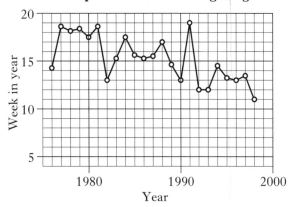

Which line in the table correctly identifies the behaviour trends shown in the graphs?

	Flight period	First sighting
A	shorter	earlier
B	longer	earlier
C	longer	later
D	shorter	later

24. The widespread distribution of DDT in the environment is a result of

A   toxicity

B   persistence

C   biotransformation

D   biological magnification.

25. In aquatic ecosystems, phosphate enrichment will **not** lead to

A   eutrophication

B   succession

C   algal bloom

D   increased biodiversity.

[END OF SECTION A]

Candidates are reminded that the answer sheet MUST be returned INSIDE the front cover of the answer book.

[Turn over for Section B on *Page ten*

SECTION B

All questions in this section should be attempted.

All answers must be written clearly and legibly in ink.

1. Some species of *Daphnia* (water fleas) are able to develop their head spines and tail spines as structural defences against predators such as fish. These structures can increase in length in response to **kairomones**, chemicals in water where the fish occur.

   One species, *Daphnia lumholtzi*, occurs naturally in freshwater habitats in Africa, Asia and Australia. It has now spread throughout North America, first appearing in lakes in the south in 1990 and reaching more northern and western lakes within four years. It is thought to have been introduced when lakes were stocked with African fish species.

   Figure 1: Illustration of *Daphnia lumholtzi* before and after exposure to kairomones

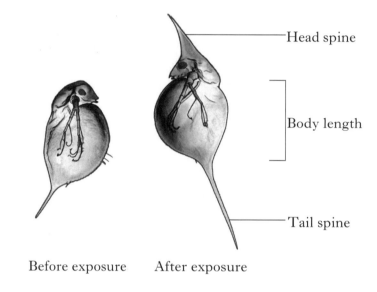

   Before exposure   After exposure

   The successful spread of *D. lumholtzi* has been attributed to its ability to develop defensive spines. To investigate the relevance of this feature to *Daphnia* survival, laboratory experiments were carried out to compare the population dynamics of *D. lumholtzi* with *Daphnia pulicaria*, the most widely distributed American species.

   All the experiments were conducted under standard conditions of temperature (20 °C) and light in identical plastic tanks. The culture medium was based on minerals and phosphate buffer made up in water of a very high purity. *Daphnia* were fed with green algae in quantities that maintained constant food availability. The density of each species was the same at the start and populations were left for several days before sampling began.

   Figure 2 shows the population changes observed from the first day of sampling in experiments set up as below:

   Experiment A: Single species alone without predators

   Experiment B: Two species together without predators

   Experiment C: Two species together with fish predators.

   Figure 3 shows the results of measuring the lengths of head spines and tail spines for the two species in culture medium either containing or lacking kairomones.

Question 1 (continued)

Figure 2: Population changes in Experiments A, B and C

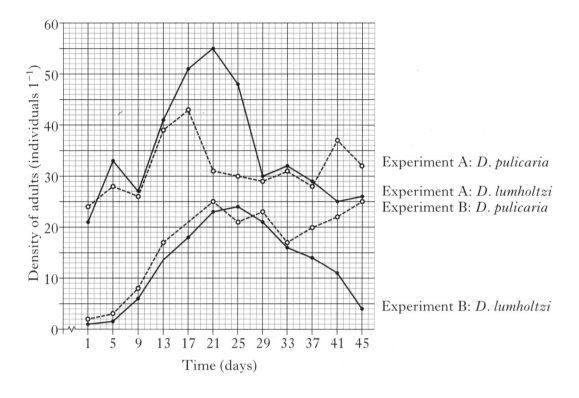

Experiment A: *D. pulicaria*

Experiment A: *D. lumholtzi*
Experiment B: *D. pulicaria*

Experiment B: *D. lumholtzi*

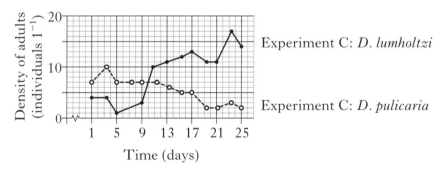

Experiment C: *D. lumholtzi*

Experiment C: *D. pulicaria*

Figure 3: Relative lengths of spines before and after exposure to kairomones

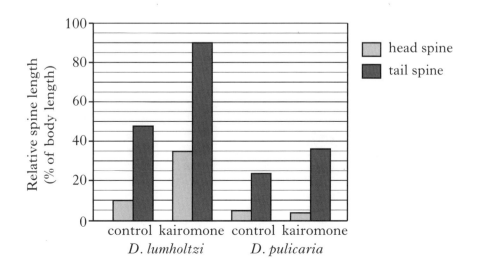

Page eleven **[Question 1 continues on *Page twelve***

Marks

Question 1 (continued)

(a) (i) Explain why *D. lumholtzi* can be described as an exotic species.   1

    (ii) State **one** damaging effect of an exotic species on an ecosystem.   1

(b) Refer to Figure 2.

    (i) Use the data at Day 41 to demonstrate that competition is a negative interaction for both species.   2

    (ii) What term could be used to describe the fate of *D. lumholtzi* in experiment B, if the trend observed from Day 33 to Day 45 continues?   1

    (iii) What evidence is there that spine formation may be affecting predator behaviour?   1

(c) Refer to Figure 3.

    (i) What appears to be the defence of *D. pulicaria* against fish predation?   1

    (ii) Suggest why relative spine lengths were used in Figure 3.   1

    (iii) For *D. lumholtzi* with a mean body length of 1·6 mm, what was the difference in length between the head spines in the control and kairomones cultures?   1

    (iv) Compare the response of the two species to the presence of kairomones.   2

(d) Spine formation is a structural defence against predators. Give **two** defences against predators in which the mechanisms depend on coloration.   2

                                                   (13)

2. Discuss the flow of energy through ecosystems.   (5)

[Question 3 is on fold-out *Page thirteen*

Marks

3. Much of the heather moorland in Scotland is an unstable, man-made ecosystem. Heather moorland is maintained by sheep grazing and by burning to promote the growth of new heather. If these activities ceased, succession would result in stable woodland communities.

   (a) What term is used to describe a stable woodland community?   1

   (b) Give one reason why stability increases as succession proceeds from heather moorland to woodland.   1

   (c) Large areas of heather moorland are under threat from bracken, a type of fern that spreads vigorously by means of underground storage organs called rhizomes. Bracken can shade out neighbouring plants and it produces toxic compounds, some of which can reduce the germination and growth of other plant species. The spread of bracken on many moorland sites has been limited by mechanical control measures (cutting and rolling) and the use of the herbicide *asulam*.

   Figure: Heather (*Calluna vulgaris*) being invaded by bracken (*Pteridium aquilinum*)

heather

bracken

   (i) What aspect of bracken's success can be attributed to interference competition?   1

   (ii) Why are mechanical control measures by themselves unlikely to be successful?   1

   (iii) An EU ban on the use of *asulam* came into effect at the end of 2011. Suggest **one** reason why such a ban would be imposed.   1

   (5)

Marks

4. Animals that live under polar sea-ice benefit from adaptations that allow them to survive changes in the salinity of their immediate environment as the ice freezes and thaws. The crustacean *Gammarus wilkitzkii* is a dominant species of the Arctic ice community.

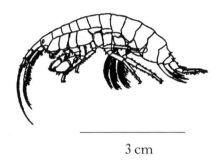

3 cm

During the summer, as sea-ice melts, this species experiences low salinity and during sea-ice growth in the winter it is exposed to high salinity.

Figure 1 shows the rate of oxygen consumption of this animal when transferred to water of varying salinity. Figure 2 shows ion concentrations in its body fluids at the higher salinities.

Figure 1

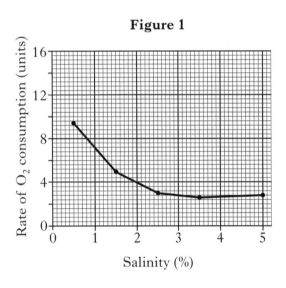

Figure 2

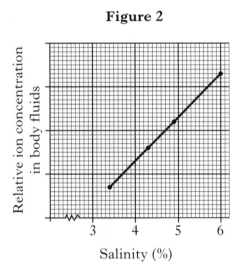

(a) Refer to Figure 1. Explain how the data suggest that *Gammarus wilkitzkii* is a regulator in salinities up to 2·5%.   2

(b) Refer to Figure 2.

   (i) What term is used to describe an organism that shows this type of physiological response?   1

   (ii) Increasing concentrations of ions in body fluids lower the temperature at which these fluids will freeze. Suggest how the response shown in Figure 2 would aid the survival of *G. wilkitzkii* during winter.   1

(c) Another crustacean, *Parathemisto libellula*, is unable to tolerate or resist salinity variations. How would this affect the habitat range that it could occupy?   1

   (5)

Marks

5. Cholesterol is an important component of cell membranes and a starter molecule in the formation of steroid hormones.

   (a) Give **one** role of cholesterol in cell membranes.

   1

   (b) When cholesterol accumulates in the wall of an artery, the plaque that forms reduces the internal diameter of the vessel. Plaque formation (atherosclerosis) is a major cause of heart disease. *Statins* are taken to reduce blood cholesterol and are one of the most commonly prescribed medications.

   Cholesterol is synthesised by cells in a sequence of steps starting with acetyl-CoA from the Krebs cycle. The step that limits the rate of production is near the start and is catalysed by the enzyme *HMG-CoA reductase*, as illustrated below.

   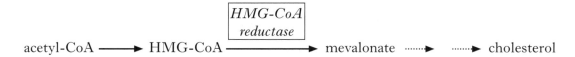

   HMG-CoA reductase

   acetyl-CoA ⟶ HMG-CoA ⟶ mevalonate ┄┄▶ ┄┄▶ cholesterol

   (i) In this pathway, a form of end-product inhibition occurs in which increasing cholesterol promotes the destruction of HMG-CoA reductase.

      Describe how end-product inhibition would be achieved if the enzyme was allosteric.

      2

   (ii) Statins are *competitive* inhibitors of HMG-CoA reductase.

      Explain how they would reduce cholesterol formation.

      1

   (iii) The graph below shows results of an experiment done in 1976 on three forms of a substance, ML-236, extracted from a fungal culture. The experiment was assessing how well these substances inhibit cholesterol formation, the key requirement for a potential statin.

   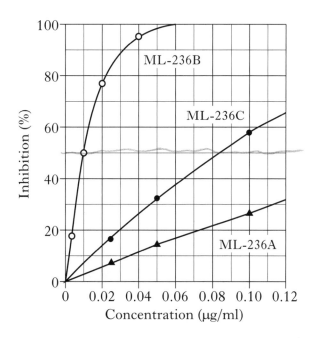

   Use data for 50% inhibition to compare the effectiveness of the three molecules as potential statins.

   2

   (6)

Marks

6. During the cell cycle, proteins called *cyclins* are made and destroyed in a fixed sequence. As their concentrations change, they activate enzymes that cause the dynamic events of the next stage to proceed.

The diagram below shows how cell cycle phases and checkpoints (1, 2 and 3) relate to changes in the level of one type of cyclin, *M-cyclin*.

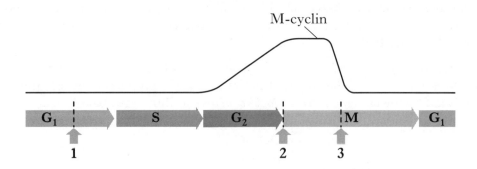

(a) M-cyclin is part of the protein complex MPF. What is the role of MPF?   1

(b) What is controlled at checkpoint 3 on the diagram?   1

(c) Use the diagram to suggest how M-cyclin contributes to the progress of the cell cycle.   1

(3)

Marks

7. Fragments of DNA between restriction sites can vary in length depending on the number of repeating units present. DNA profiling identifies the number of repeating units between the restriction sites on each chromosome.

   The diagram below shows fragments from a pair of homologous chromosomes for an individual with four repeating units on one chromosome and two on the other chromosome. The genotype for this individual is described as 4, 2.

   (a) Orphans (A, B, C, D) from a war zone, believed to be from the same family, were being relocated back to grandparents. DNA profiling was used to check the family tree. The results are shown below.

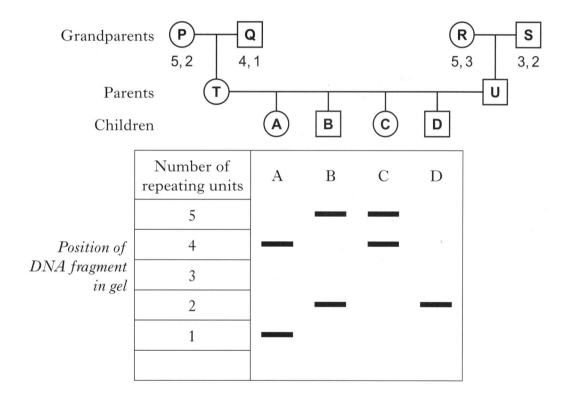

   (i) Explain the result for child D.   1

   (ii) Which child is **not** related to both sets of grandparents? Use the results to justify your answer.   1

   (b) Explain the role of probing in the production of a DNA profile.   1

       (3)

[Turn over

Marks

8. Answer **either** A **or** B.

   A. Give an account of the procedures involved in producing transgenic plants. Use the following headings:

     (*a*) plant production by tissue culture;   **5**

     (*b*) the use of *Agrobacterium*;   **4**

     (*c*) modification of plasmids.   **6**

OR   **(15)**

   B. Give an account of proteins in the following contexts:

     (*a*) membranes;   **5**

     (*b*) cell signalling;   **5**

     (*c*) cytoskeleton.   **5**

                                                (15)

[END OF SECTION B]

[Turn over for Section C on *Page twenty*

Marks

SECTION C

Candidates should attempt questions on <u>one</u> unit, <u>either</u> Biotechnology <u>or</u> Animal Behaviour <u>or</u> Physiology, Health and Exercise.

The questions on Biotechnology can be found on pages 20–22.

The questions on Animal Behaviour can be found on pages 23–25.

The questions on Physiology, Health and Exercise can be found on pages 26–28.

All answers must be written clearly and legibly in ink.

Labelled diagrams may be used where appropriate.

BIOTECHNOLOGY

1. A study was carried out to investigate the growth rate of the bacterium *Escherichia coli* (*E. coli*) in different growth media. A single colony of bacteria was used to inoculate either complex broth or minimal medium to which was added one of a variety of carbon sources. Cell numbers were estimated using a colorimeter to measure the turbidity of the culture during growth. The generation time for each culture is shown in the table.

Growth medium	Generation time (minutes)
complex broth	22
minimal medium + glucose	40
minimal medium + succinate	67
minimal medium + ethanoate	120

(a) (i)   What is meant by the term *generation time*?   1

(ii) Give **two** general conclusions about the effects of growth medium on the generation time of *E. coli*.   2

(b) Calculate the growth rate constant for *E. coli* growing in minimal medium containing ethanoate. (ln2 = 0·693)   1

(c) (i)   State **one** disadvantage of the method used to estimate cell numbers.   1

(ii) Name an alternative method for obtaining cell number in bacterial cultures.   1

(6)

2. Silage is an important winter feed for cattle. Give an account of the production of silage.   **(5)**

Marks

BIOTECHNOLOGY (continued)

3. Antibiotics can be produced by growing micro-organisms in culture media made from waste materials. For example, apple *pomace* is a waste left over after juice extraction and it contains peel, seeds and other solid parts. Waste materials are dried and ground into a powder that can be added to culture medium in a fermenter.

    (a) The graph below shows the yield of the antibiotic *neomycin* produced using media containing a variety of agricultural waste products.

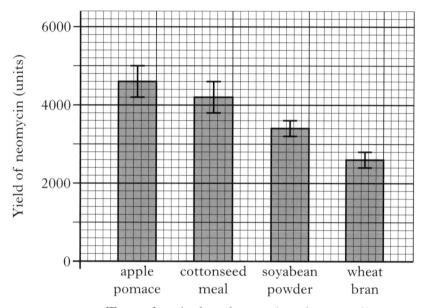

Type of agricultural waste in culture medium

    (i)   It was concluded that medium containing apple pomace gave a higher yield of neomycin than media containing the other waste products. Comment on the validity of this conclusion.   2

    (ii) This study was carried out in India where it is estimated that one million tonnes of apple pomace is produced each year. Suggest **two** reasons why it is desirable to use this material in the production of antibiotics.   2

    (b) Neomycin is a bactericidal antibiotic. Describe how its action would differ from a bacteriostatic antibiotic.   1

    (5)

[Turn over

Marks

BIOTECHNOLOGY (continued)

4. Many enzymes used in biotechnology are produced industrially by fermentation using naturally occurring micro-organisms.

   (a) Name **one** industrially produced enzyme and the micro-organism used in the fermentation.   1

   (b) (i) Describe **two** conditions that need to be controlled during the fermentation process used to produce enzymes.   1

   (ii) Give **one** method used in the recovery of enzymes from the fermentation culture.   1

   (c) Explain what is meant when an industrial enzyme is described as a *secondary metabolite*.   1

   (4)

[End of *Biotechnology* questions. *Animal Behaviour* questions start on Page 23]

Marks

SECTION C (continued)

ANIMAL BEHAVIOUR

1. Sexual selection in the dung beetle *Onthophagus sagittarius* was investigated in the laboratory.

Male (left) and female dung beetles.

Beetles were paired by randomly selecting males and females, and the pairs were placed in breeding chambers. Mating success in relation to the frequency of courtship behaviour was recorded for large and small males.

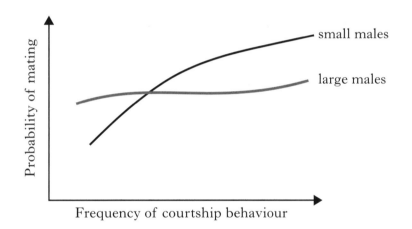

(a) From the results, describe how female choice changes in relation to male size.　　　1

(b) What terms apply to the following measurements during the experiment:

   (i) time from introduction until first courtship;　　　1

   (ii) total time of courtship?　　　1

(c) Male and female dung beetles can be distinguished by their horns. What term can be used to describe this difference in appearance?　　　1

(d) Females in many species are relatively inconspicuous. Explain why this is beneficial to them.　　　2

(6)

[Turn over

Marks

ANIMAL BEHAVIOUR (continued)

2. Most of the behaviour of the fruitfly *Drosophila melanogaster* is determined by "nature" rather than "nurture".

    (*a*) Explain why nurture has little influence on the behaviour of an invertebrate such as *Drosophila*.

    1

    (*b*) The *Drosophila* period (*per*) gene is an example of a single gene affecting behaviour. Describe the effects of this gene.

    2

    (3)

3. Discuss behaviour that maximises net energy intake by predators.

    (5)

Marks

ANIMAL BEHAVIOUR (continued)

4. Many birds that feed together in mixed-species flocks produce distinctive alarm calls which alert other flock members to the presence of predators. However, some of the flocks may contain birds that produce calls that sound similar to the alarm calls. These calls are emitted when there are no predators present and are referred to as "false alarm" calls.

    (a) Explain why true alarm calling may be regarded as altruistic behaviour.   2

    (b) State why the evolution of true alarm calls **cannot** be the result of kin selection alone.   1

    (c) Suggest a benefit to the caller of using false alarm calls.   1

    (d) A study investigated true and false alarm calls of the racket-tailed drongo (*Dicrurus paradiseus*). The calls were recorded and played to the orange-billed babbler (*Turdoides rufescens*), a species that regularly feeds in the same flocks. The graph shows the responses of the babblers to both types of call.

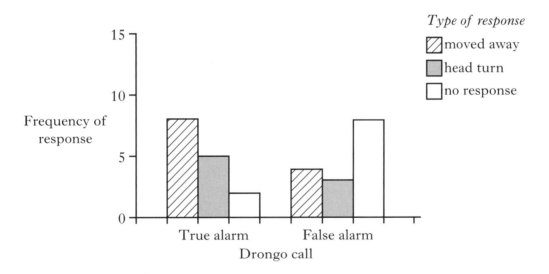

    From the graph select information to show that babblers are able to distinguish between the false and true alarm calls of the drongos.   1

    (e) The study involved wild babblers in their natural habitat. Suggest why the researchers used a method that involved selecting a different individual babbler for each measurement.   1

    (6)

[End of *Animal Behaviour* questions. *Physiology, Health and Exercise* questions start on Page 26]

[Turn over

Marks

SECTION C (continued)

PHYSIOLOGY, HEALTH AND EXERCISE

1. Coronary heart disease (CHD) is caused by restriction of blood flow in vessels that supply oxygenated blood to heart muscle.

    (*a*) Describe the changes in blood vessel walls that lead to CHD.   2

    (*b*) Give **two** modifiable risk factors for the development of CHD.   1

    (*c*) The table shows the incidence of CHD in two categories of male employees in the 1950s.

Age (years)	CHD rate per 1000	
	Postmen	*Office workers*
35–44	0·3	0·4
45–54	2·7	2·9
55–65	4·6	6·5

    Give **two** general conclusions about CHD that can be drawn from the data.   2

    (5)

2. Discuss the effects of exercise on the development of osteoporosis.   **(4)**

Marks

PHYSIOLOGY, HEALTH AND EXERCISE (continued)

3. (*a*) (i) Give **one** reason for assessing body composition.

1

(ii) What **two** measurements are required to estimate body composition using densitometry?

1

(*b*) The BMI value is used routinely in the assessment of an individual's body composition. State **one** limitation of using BMI for this purpose.

1

(*c*) Percentage body fat can be measured accurately using a method called *dual X-ray absorption* (DXA). The graph shows "best fit" lines when BMI values are correlated with measured % body fat.

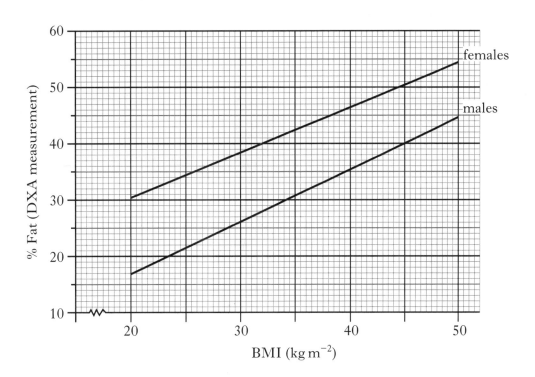

(i) What are the BMI values of a man and a woman who both have 40% body fat?

1

(ii) Recently an improved way of estimating % body fat has been developed. It involves calculating the body adiposity index (BAI) using the formula below. The calculated BAI equals the % body fat.

$$\text{BAI} = \left(\frac{\text{Hip circumference (cm)}}{\text{Height (m)} \times \sqrt{\text{Height (m)}}} \right) - 18$$

A woman with a BMI value of 27 (kg m^{-2}) has a hip circumference 105 cm and height 1·69 m. Compare the predicted value of % body fat obtained using her BMI with that obtained using the more accurate BAI.

2

(6)

[Turn over for Question 4 on *Page twenty-eight*

Marks

PHYSIOLOGY, HEALTH AND EXERCISE (continued)

4. Elite athletes are interested in ways to improve performance in endurance events.

    (a) Give **two** changes in the performance of an athlete's heart arising from endurance training.

    2

    (b) In a study, volunteers ate a mixed diet for three days and then measured endurance by exercising to exhaustion. Over the next three days they ate a low carbohydrate diet and again measured endurance. Over a further three days they ate a high carbohydrate diet and exercised to exhaustion for a third time.

    The Figure shows glycogen concentration in skeletal muscle before and after the endurance testing for each stage of the diet programme. The Table shows the time to exhaustion as *exercise duration*.

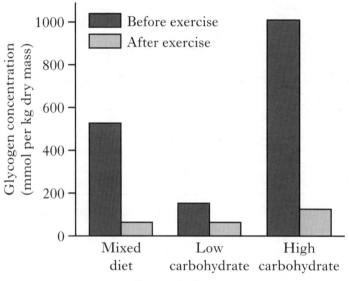

Stage of diet programme	Exercise duration (mins)
Mixed diet	126
Low carbohydrate	59
High carbohydrate	189

    (i)   What evidence supports the conclusion that increased muscle glycogen improved endurance?

    1

    (ii) What term is used for exercise testing that takes athletes to exhaustion?

    1

    (iii) Give an example of a situation where it would **not** be appropriate for an individual to exercise to exhaustion.

    1

    (5)

[END OF QUESTION PAPER]

ADVANCED HIGHER

2014

[BLANK PAGE]

X007/13/02

NATIONAL
QUALIFICATIONS
2014

FRIDAY, 16 MAY
1.00 PM – 3.30 PM

BIOLOGY
ADVANCED HIGHER

SECTION A—Questions 1–25 (25 marks)

Instructions for completion of Section A are given on *Page two*.

SECTIONS B AND C

The answer to each question should be written in ink in the answer book provided. Any additional paper (if used) should be placed inside the front cover of the answer book.

Rough work should be scored through.

Section B (55 marks)

All questions should be attempted. Candidates should note that Question 8 contains a choice.

Question 1 is on Pages 10, 11 and 12. Question 2 is on Page 12 and Question 3 is on Page 13. Pages 12 and 13 are fold-out pages.

Section C (20 marks)

Candidates should attempt the questions in **one** unit, **either** Biotechnology **or** Animal Behaviour **or** Physiology, Health and Exercise.

Read carefully

1 Check that the answer sheet provided is for **Biology Advanced Higher (Section A)**.

2 For this section of the examination you must use an **HB pencil** and, where necessary, an eraser.

3 Check that the answer sheet you have been given has **your name**, **date of birth**, **SCN** (Scottish Candidate Number) and **Centre Name** printed on it.

   Do not change any of these details.

4 If any of this information is wrong, tell the Invigilator immediately.

5 If this information is correct, **print** your name and seat number in the boxes provided.

6 The answer to each question is **either** A, B, C or D. Decide what your answer is, then, using your pencil, put a horizontal line in the space provided (see sample question below).

7 There is **only one correct** answer to each question.

8 Any rough working should be done on the question paper or the rough working sheet, **not** on your answer sheet.

9 At the end of the examination, put the **answer sheet for Section A inside the front cover of the answer book**.

Sample Question

Which of the following molecules contains six carbon atoms?

A Glucose

B Pyruvic acid

C Ribulose bisphosphate

D Acetyl coenzyme A

The correct answer is **A**—Glucose. The answer **A** has been clearly marked in **pencil** with a horizontal line (see below).

Changing an answer

If you decide to change your answer, carefully erase your first answer and using your pencil, fill in the answer you want. The answer below has been changed to **D**.

SECTION A

All questions in this section should be attempted.

Answers should be given on the separate answer sheet provided.

1. Which of the following is the main component of bacterial cell walls?

   A   Cellulose

   B   Phospholipid

   C   Polysaccharide

   D   Peptidoglycan

2. In *E. coli*, DNA in the nucleoid is 1·7 mm long and the cell is typically 2 μm in length. How many times longer is the DNA compared to the cell?

   A   0·85

   B   1·18

   C   850

   D   1176

3. The organelles in the list below can be found in a range of cells.

   1   Endoplasmic reticulum

   2   Golgi apparatus

   3   Mitochondria

   4   Ribosomes

   Which of these organelles would be found in both eukaryotic and prokaryotic cells?

   A   4 only

   B   1 and 4 only

   C   1, 3 and 4 only

   D   1, 2, 3 and 4

4. Which of the following occurs during **S** phase of the cell cycle?

   A   The cytoplasm divides.

   B   The DNA replicates.

   C   Two identical nuclei are formed.

   D   The nuclear membrane forms.

5. The table below shows the number of cells from a cell culture at different stages in the cell cycle.

Stage	Number of cells
Interphase	2240
Prophase	300
Metaphase	180
Anaphase	40
Telophase	40

   The mitotic index for the sample is

   A   8%

   B   20%

   C   25%

   D   32%.

6. Which of the following describes the action of oncogenes?

   A   They cause cell proliferation resulting in tumour formation.

   B   They encode the proteins that limit cell division.

   C   They restrict cell division at checkpoints.

   D   They switch genes on during cell differentiation.

[Turn over

7. The table below shows the results of an investigation to work out the best combination of auxin and cytokinin for promoting organ growth from explants in plant tissue culture.

Concentration of auxin (μmol L^{-1})	Concentration of cytokinin (μmol L^{-1})	Appearance of tissue after incubation	Summary of effect
10	0		No growth
10	0·1		Roots growing
10	1·0		Disorganised growth
10	2·5		Several shoots
10	10·0		A few shoots; considerable growth
10	50·0		Limited, disorganised growth

In the culture medium, what ratio of auxin to cytokinin is most successful for this plant?

A   1 : 1

B   4 : 1

C   10 : 1

D   100 : 1

8. Fatty acids and glycerol are joined in a triglyceride by

   A   hydrogen bonds

   B   peptide bonds

   C   ester linkages

   D   glycosidic linkages.

9. Which of the following describes the structure of cytosine?

   A   A purine base with a single-ring structure

   B   A purine base with a double-ring structure

   C   A pyrimidine base with a single-ring structure

   D   A pyrimidine base with a double-ring structure

10. The genome of a cell contains 3×10^9 base pairs. Only 1·5% of the genome codes for proteins.

    How many amino acids are encoded by this genome?

    A $1·5 \times 10^7$

    B $4·5 \times 10^7$

    C $5·0 \times 10^{10}$

    D $4·5 \times 10^{11}$

11. The mechanism of action of the sodium-potassium pump includes the following events:

    P   membrane protein loses a phosphate group

    Q   potassium binds to membrane protein

    R   potassium ions are released

    S   membrane protein shape is restored.

    The correct sequence of these events is

    A   P, Q, R, S

    B   P, Q, S, R

    C   Q, P, R, S

    D   Q, P, S, R

12. The diagram below represents the molecules involved in an enzyme reaction.

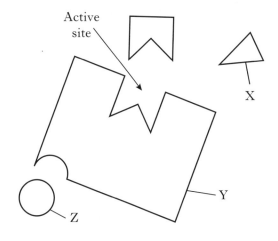

Which line in the table correctly identifies the molecules?

	X	Y	Z
A	competitive inhibitor	enzyme	non-competitive inhibitor
B	competitive inhibitor	substrate	non-competitive inhibitor
C	non-competitive inhibitor	enzyme	competitive inhibitor
D	non-competitive inhibitor	substrate	competitive inhibitor

13. Which of the following stages in the polymerase chain reaction (PCR) is carried out at 95 °C?

    A   Annealing of primers

    B   Separation of DNA strands

    C   Formation of phosphodiester bonds

    D   Complementary base pairing

[Turn over

14. In aquatic ecosystems the amount of sunlight absorbed by water increases with depth.

Absorption by seawater is greater than absorption by fresh water.

Which of the following graphs represents the relationship between depth and light intensity in fresh water and seawater?

Key   —————— sea water

- - - - - - fresh water

A
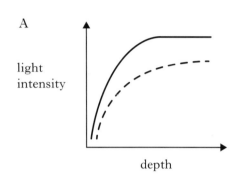

B
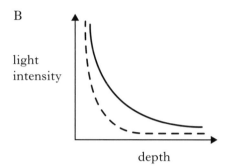

C
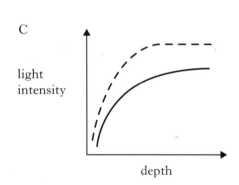

D
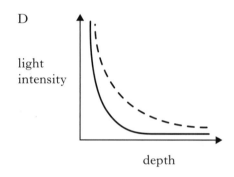

15. Detritivores play an important role in the circulation of nutrients in the soil.

Which line in the table below shows the correct classification of detritivores and the product they form in the soil?

	Classification	Product
A	invertebrates	ammonia
B	bacteria	humus
C	invertebrates	humus
D	bacteria	ammonia

16. The following micro-organisms are involved in nitrate formation in ecosystems.

1   Cyanobacteria

2   *Nitrosomonas*

3   *Nitrobacter*

4   *Rhizobium*

Which line in the table matches correctly the micro-organisms and their roles?

	Nitrogen fixation	Nitrification
A	1 and 3	2 and 4
B	2 and 3	1 and 4
C	2 and 4	1 and 3
D	1 and 4	2 and 3

17. In the following table "+" indicates a benefit and "−" indicates a cost or negative effect on an organism in a relationship. "0" indicates neither benefit nor cost.

For which of the relationships in the table is the benefit/cost shown **incorrectly**?

	Relationship	Benefit/cost
A	commensalism	+/0
B	competition	+/−
C	parasitism	+/−
D	predation	+/−

18. In Africa, a bird called the honey-guide eats beeswax but can only feed when a honey-badger has broken open a wild bee nest to feed on the honey. The honey-guide locates the bee nest and leads the honey-badger to it.

The relationship between the honey-guide and the honey-badger is an example of

A   parasitism

B   competition

C   commensalism

D   mutualism.

19. The production of toxic chemicals by one species of plant to prevent the growth of other plant species is an example of

A   interspecific exploitation competition

B   interspecific interference competition

C   intraspecific exploitation competition

D   intraspecific interference competition.

20. The Sea Star *Pisaster ochraceous* is a key predator of the rocky intertidal zone on the coast of Washington State, USA. It feeds on mussels and other invertebrates in rock pools. One of the lines in the graph below shows the effect of removing *Pisaster* from a rock pool in 1993.

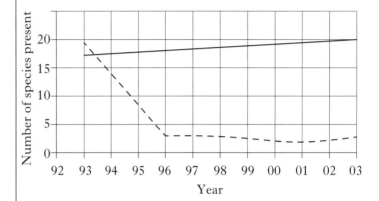

Which line in the table correctly describes the results?

	Line P	Line Q	Role of Pisaster
A	with *Pisaster*	without *Pisaster*	decreases species diversity
B	with *Pisaster*	without *Pisaster*	increases species diversity
C	without *Pisaster*	with *Pisaster*	increases species diversity
D	without *Pisaster*	with *Pisaster*	decreases species diversity

[Turn over

21. Which of the graphs below represents the relationship between the intensity of rabbit grazing and the diversity of plant species in a series of grassland plots?

A

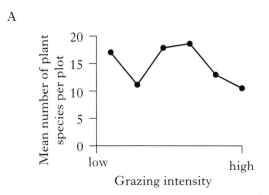

B

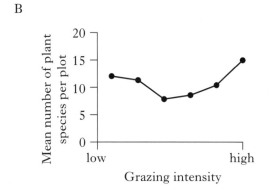

C

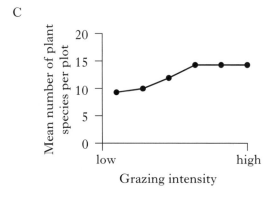

D

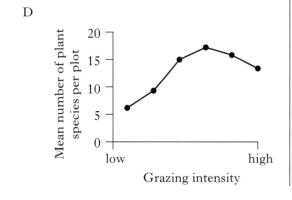

22. Diagram A shows three burrowing animals that live at different depths in Scottish beaches. They are eaten by various wading birds such as those illustrated in Diagram B.

Diagram A

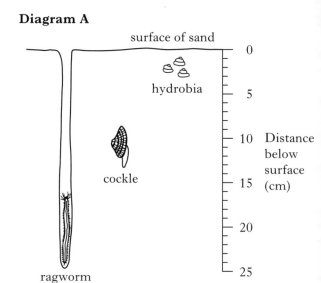

Diagram B

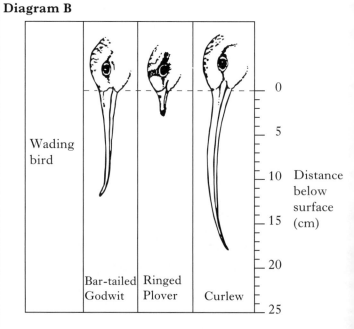

Which of the following is a consequence of the different lengths of the waders' beaks?

A   Resource partitioning

B   Competitive exclusion

C   Exploitation competition

D   Interspecific competition

23. The table below shows the results of a population survey of *Hydrobia* snails using a quadrat in five random positions on a muddy beach.

Quadrat	1	2	3	4	5
Number of snails	1800	2600	2100	1900	1600

The quadrat measured 50 cm × 50 cm.

What was the average density of *Hydrobia* per square metre?

A   2000

B   4000

C   8000

D   10 000

24. Scarlet kingsnakes are non-venomous and live in the same area as the venomous eastern coral snakes. Both species have red, yellow and black ring markings.

Which line in the table correctly describes the relationship between these two species?

	Model	Mimic	Type of mimicry
A	coral snake	scarlet kingsnake	Batesian
B	scarlet kingsnake	coral snake	Batesian
C	coral snake	scarlet kingsnake	Mullerian
D	scarlet kingsnake	coral snake	Mullerian

25. Suspended development of insects in response to the adverse environmental conditions of winter is a form of

A   predictive dormancy called hibernation

B   predictive dormancy called diapause

C   consequential dormancy called diapause

D   consequential dormancy called hibernation.

[END OF SECTION A]

Candidates are reminded that the answer sheet MUST be returned INSIDE the front cover of the answer book.

[Turn over for SECTION B on *Page ten*

SECTION B

All questions in this section should be attempted.

All answers must be written clearly and legibly in ink.

1. Two types of muscle, red and white, can be distinguished by their colour in samples of fresh tissue and can be easily separated. Red muscle cells obtain energy mainly using aerobic respiration: they have many large mitochondria and a good supply of oxygen. White muscle cells obtain energy mainly by anaerobic respiration: they have fewer mitochondria and a poorer oxygen supply. In both muscle types, glucose is the substrate for respiration. It is widely thought that the mechanism of glucose transport into these cells is the step that limits their ability to use glucose, and it is considered that red muscle cells have a greater capacity for glucose transport than white muscle cells.

   Glucose diffuses into cells through glucose transporters (GLUTs), which are protein molecules embedded in cell membranes. There are several types of GLUT. GLUT1 is responsible for glucose uptake in all cells; the membranes of muscle and fat cells also contain GLUT4.

   The study below investigated the contribution of these two GLUTs to glucose uptake in red and white muscle cells, before and after exposure to insulin. Figure 1 shows the effect of insulin on glucose transport in the two types of muscle.

   An extract of membranes from the muscle cells was centrifuged to separate it into two portions, plasma membrane (PM) and the internal membranes (IM) from the cytoplasm. The protein components of the membranes were separated by gel electrophoresis and blotted. The blots were exposed to radioactively-labelled antibodies specific for each of the two GLUT proteins, to allow identification and quantification.

   Figure 2 shows the percentage change in total GLUT level in the two membrane fractions following the insulin treatment. In Figure 3, the blots indicate the changing abundances of the two GLUTs. Figure 4 shows the relative amount of GLUT4 in the two muscle types in response to insulin. Error bars show *standard error*.

Figure 1: Glucose transport with and without insulin	**Figure 2:** Effect of insulin on total GLUT levels
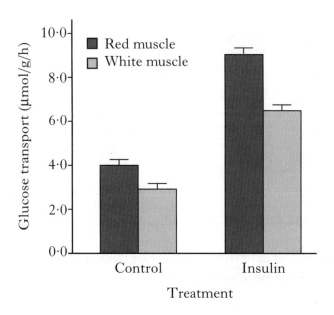	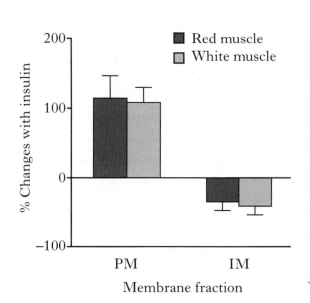

Question 1 (continued)

Figure 3: Blots showing the effect of insulin on the distribution of GLUTs 1 and 4

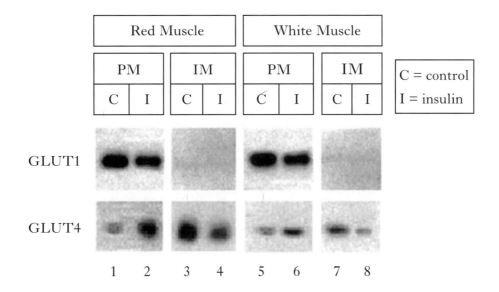

Figure 4: Relative amounts of GLUT4 quantified from several blots

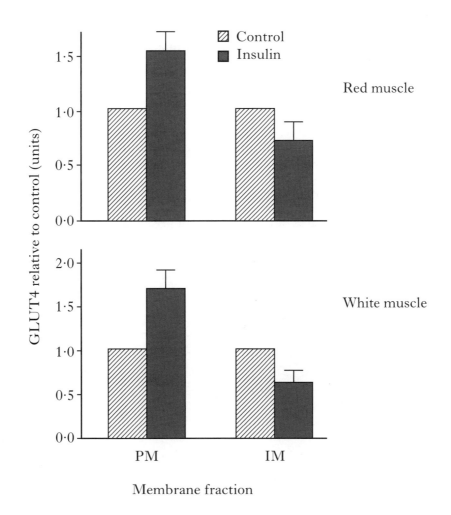

Marks

Question 1 (continued)

(a) Use data from Figure 1 to support the statement that "red muscle cells have a greater capacity for glucose transport than white muscle cells".   2

(b) Figure 2 shows that GLUT increases in the PM fraction and decreases in the IM fraction after insulin treatment.

    (i) Why is *percentage change* being used here to present the results?   1

    (ii) It was concluded that both muscle types have the same underlying GLUT response to insulin. Explain how the error bars confirm this conclusion is valid.   1

(c) Refer to Figure 3.

    (i) Describe the distribution of GLUT1 in muscle cells before insulin treatment.   1

    (ii) Give **one** conclusion about the effect of insulin treatment on GLUT1.   1

    (iii) What evidence is there that the effect of insulin on the distribution of GLUT4 is the same in both types of muscle?   1

(d) It was hypothesised that insulin triggers the transport of additional GLUT4 to the plasma membrane from storage on membranes in cytoplasm, and that this 'recruitment' mechanism is greater in red muscle cells.

Explain how the results from Figures 3 and 4 support this hypothesis.   2

(e) (i) Insulin is a hydrophilic signalling molecule. Explain why some cells are not targets in this type of signalling.   2

    (ii) Explain why the effect of insulin on GLUT4 is an example of signal transduction.   1

(f) Glucose taken up by different cell types in response to insulin can have different fates, for example muscle cells can convert glucose to glycogen.

    (i) State the role of glycogen in cells.   1

    (ii) Give **two** features of the structure of glycogen.   1

        (14)

2. Transgenic plants can be grown from modified protoplasts. Describe how plasmids from *Agrobacterium* are engineered and used to produce modified protoplasts.   **(4)**

[Question 3 is on *Page thirteen*

Marks

3. Tubulin is described as a *dimer* because it is made of two polypeptide subunits, alpha-tubulin and beta-tubulin. Both subunits contain GTP, a molecule that is similar to ATP but has the base guanine instead of adenine. A representation of alpha-tubulin is shown below.

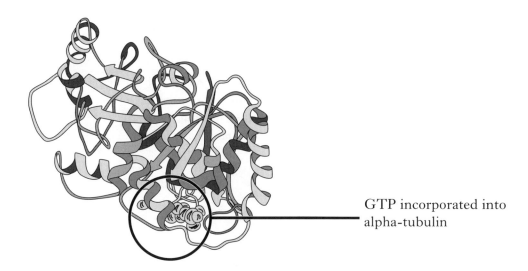

GTP incorporated into alpha-tubulin

Microtubules are made of assembled tubulin. Microtubules can extend at one end by the addition of tubulin dimers provided there are enough present.

(a) What term is used to describe a component, such as GTP, embedded in a polypeptide?   1

(b) During mitosis:

   (i) to which structures do the two ends of a spindle fibre normally attach?   1

   (ii) what is the role of spindle microtubules in anaphase?   1

(c) (i) A new drug, *eribulin*, has recently been approved as a treatment for some advanced cancers. Eribulin, introduced into the bloodstream, appears to have two effects in dividing cells: it blocks the growing ends of microtubules and it binds to available tubulin dimers.

   Suggest why cells treated with eribulin might fail the M checkpoint in the cell cycle.   1

   (ii) Suggest **one** disadvantage of treating tumours with drugs that target cell division.   1

   (5)

Marks

4. The enzyme *enteropeptidase* brings about the conversion of trypsinogen to trypsin.

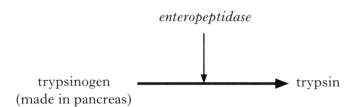

enteropeptidase

trypsinogen   ————————▶   trypsin
(made in pancreas)

Enteropeptidase is made in cells lining the duodenum but only after partially digested food has moved on from the stomach and when pancreatic juice has entered the gut. This key enzyme is not free to move; it remains bound to plasma membranes of the cells that make it. A powerful trypsin inhibitor is present in pancreatic juice, even though no trypsin is present.

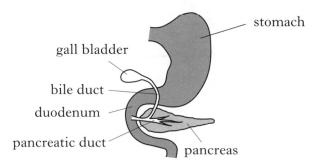

- stomach

gall bladder

bile duct

duodenum

pancreatic duct

pancreas

(a) What term describes the activation carried out by enteropeptidase?   1

(b) Name the type of reaction carried out on a peptide bond by a protease such as trypsin.   1

(c) Why is it important that active trypsin is produced only after trypsinogen has left the pancreas?   1

(d) Enteropeptidase cuts trypsinogen after the amino acid lysine, in a unique position where it is bonded to isoleucine. Trypsin attacks points in any polypeptide where either of the amino acids lysine or arginine appear.

Explain why trypsin formation accelerates once trypsin production has started.   1

(4)

5. (a) Mammals and birds are homeotherms; they maintain a constant body temperature. For this adaptation, give

    (i) one cost;

    (ii) one benefit.   2

(b) The body fluids of sea urchins are isotonic with seawater, that is, they have the same solute concentration as their surroundings.

What term is used to describe an organism that has this type of interaction with the environment?

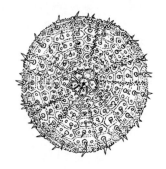

1

(3)

Marks

6. Pesticides are widely used in intensive food production.

   (a) Explain the role of pesticides in intensive crop production.

   1

   (b) Give **one** feature of a pesticide that can help to reduce undesirable effects on the environment.

   1

   (c) Bumble-bees (*Bombus* species) are important pollinators of crop plants and wild flowers. Since 2006 there have been increasing numbers of reports of bee colonies suddenly dying off with a condition referred to as *colony collapse disorder*.

   (i) Colony collapse disorder has been linked to the widespread use of *neonicotinoid* insecticides.

   The graph below shows the changes in usage of neonicotinoids since their introduction into the UK in 1995.

   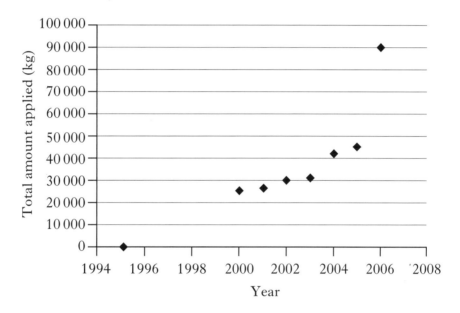

   Calculate the percentage increase in neonicotinoid usage between 2002 and 2006.

   1

   (ii) Bee behaviour, however, may also contribute to colony loss. Bumble-bee colonies contain up to 100 individuals and the bees forage no more than a few hundred metres from their nests. Most of their food (pollen and nectar) is used immediately and very little is stored.

   Suggest **one** way intensive crop production could be planned to improve the conservation of bumble-bees. Explain your suggestion.

   2

   (5)

[Turn over

Marks

7. As global warming proceeds, gradual changes in community composition of ecosystems are expected to occur.

   (a) Explain how a gradual increase in sea temperature leads to coral bleaching.

   2

   (b) Recently it has been proposed that global warming is increasing the frequency of *extreme weather events*, such as droughts and heatwaves. It is not known if these intense, localised conditions have any significant impact on ecosystems.

   The community composition of coral reefs was monitored over several years in Jurien Bay on the west coast of Australia. During 2011, warmer seawater moved from the tropical north into cooler, southern areas.

   Figure 1 shows the mean water temperature recorded each week in 2011 and the mean for the five preceding years. Figure 2 shows the abundance of seaweed species that form a floating canopy and those that cover the seabed as 'turf'.

Figure 1: Sea temperatures

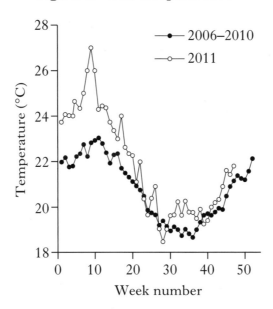

Figure 2: Abundance of Seaweeds

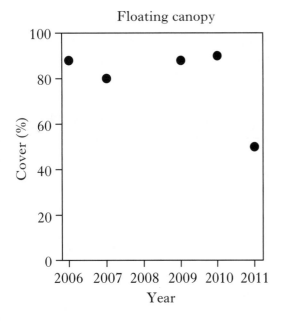

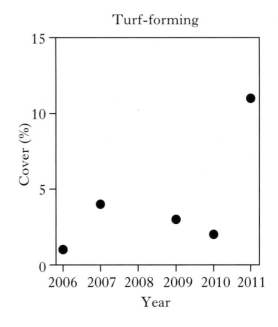

Marks

7. (*b*) (continued)

    (i) Using the data, show that there was a sea temperature "spike" in 2011.   **1**

    (ii) What impact does the sea temperature spike appear to have had on the plant community in Jurien Bay?   **1**

  (*c*) A permanent change in an external factor such as temperature can result in the formation of a new climax community. What term describes this outcome?   **1**

                                                            (5)

8. Answer **either** A **or** B.

  A. Give an account of energy in ecosystems under the following headings:

    (i) energy fixation;   **6**

    (ii) flow of energy through trophic levels.   **9**

                                                           (15)

OR

  B. Give an account of the pollution of fresh-water ecosystems arising from the:

    (i) use of fossil fuels;   **5**

    (ii) release of toxic pollutants;   **5**

    (iii) release of biodegradable organic pollutants.   **5**

                                                           (15)

[END OF SECTION B]

[Turn over for SECTION C on *Page eighteen*

Marks

SECTION C

Candidates should attempt questions on <u>one</u> unit, <u>either</u> Biotechnology <u>or</u> Animal Behaviour <u>or</u> Physiology, Health and Exercise.

The questions on Biotechnology can be found on pages 18–20.

The questions on Animal Behaviour can be found on pages 22–24.

The questions on Physiology, Health and Exercise can be found on pages 25–27.

All answers must be written clearly and legibly in ink.

Labelled diagrams may be used where appropriate.

BIOTECHNOLOGY

1. The bacterium *Escherichia coli* (*E. coli*) can use a variety of different sugars as an energy source during growth. The graph shows the typical growth curve obtained when *E. coli* is cultured in a medium containing both glucose and lactose.

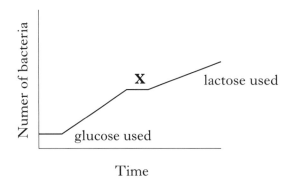

(a) Give **one** method that could be used to determine cell numbers in the production of a bacterial growth curve.   1

(b) What term describes the two-phase pattern of growth shown?   1

(c) The two-phase growth results from the effects of two regulatory proteins, *lac* repressor and CAP, on the lac operon. Explain the role of these proteins in producing the second phase of growth:

   (i) *lac* repressor;

   (ii) CAP.   2

(d) Suggest an explanation for the shape of the graph at position X.   1

                                                        (5)

2. Describe how micro-organisms are manipulated and grown in the industrial production of the enzyme chymosin.   **(5)**

Marks

BIOTECHNOLOGY (continued)

3. Figure 1 shows steps in the production of a monoclonal antibody.

   Figure 1

   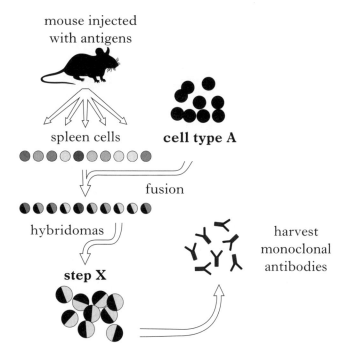

   In the treatment of disease, monoclonal antibodies can be attached to toxic components to create "magic bullets". One example of this, shown in Figure 2, uses a component that emits damaging radiation.

   Figure 2

   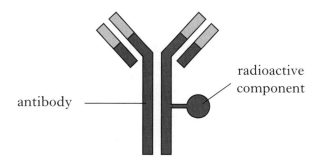

   (a) (i)   Name cell type A and explain the role of these cells in the production of monoclonal antibodies.   2

        (ii) How are unfused Type A cells eliminated at step X?   1

   (b) Explain how this magic bullet would work in the treatment of a tumour.   2

                                                                                    (5)

                                                                    [Turn over

Marks

BIOTECHNOLOGY (continued)

4. Yeast autolysis is a process in which yeast biomass undergoes degradation by internal enzymes. The autolysate produced can have a variety of uses, including the production of flavourings for foods.

Ribonucleic acid (RNA) is degraded by autolysis in the production of the flavour-enhancing molecules IMP and GMP, as shown in the flow chart below. However, autolysis must be carefully controlled to prevent the RNA being degraded too far.

The table below shows the results of a study into the effects of different heat treatments on the autolysis process in the yeast *Kluyveromyces marxianus*.

Treatment of cells		Soluble protein in autolysate (g per litre)	Partially degraded RNA in autolysate (mg per litre)
Temperature (°C)	Time (hours)		
35	15	19.4 ± 0.4	not detected
	30	18.8 ± 1.0	not detected
50	15	18.8 ± 0.5	285 ± 30
	30	18.4 ± 0.2	430 ± 10

(a) How do the data support the conclusion that increasing the temperature from 35°C to 50°C had no effect on the release of protein during autolysis?   1

(b) (i) What evidence is there that some treatments have totally degraded the RNA molecules?   1

   (ii) Which treatment would be best for maximising the production of GMP and IMP? Explain your choice.   2

(c) Give **one** factor, other than heat treatment, that can affect the characteristics of yeast autolysate.   1

   (5)

[End of *Biotechnology* questions.]

[Turn over for *ANIMAL BEHAVIOUR* questions on *Page twenty-two*

SECTION C (continued)

ANIMAL BEHAVIOUR

1. Some species show a tendency to remain in their home area after birth or hatching. Staying in a familiar environment for breeding can be advantageous since the risks and costs of exploring new habitats are avoided. However, the encounter rate of related individuals is high and can increase the risk of inbreeding. A mechanism to avoid inbreeding is likely to be favoured by natural selection.

    A study was carried out on European storm petrels (*Hydrobates pelagicus*), Figure 1, to see if these birds are able to distinguish between kin and non-kin individuals by odour.

    Birds were captured from their burrows and rubbed with cotton swabs to collect individual odours. A cotton swab from a related bird (kin) was placed in one 'goal' arm in a Y-maze.

    A swab from an unrelated bird (non-kin) was placed in the other goal arm. Birds placed in the entrance to the maze were allowed to make a choice by walking into one goal arm or the other. Some birds did not move from the entrance, so did not make a choice. Results for forty birds tested are shown in Figure 3.

Figure 1:   European storm petrel

Figure 2:   Y-maze

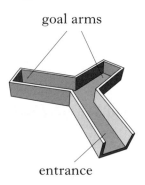

Figure 3:   Results of the Y-maze experiments

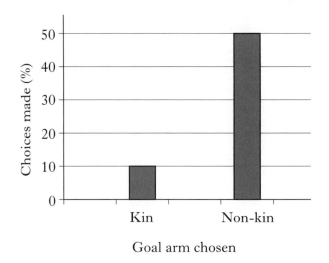

Marks

ANIMAL BEHAVIOUR (continued)

1. **(continued)**

   (*a*) (i) What conclusion can be drawn from these results? 1

   (ii) Calculate the number of birds that made no choice. 1

   (*b*) Suggest **one** precaution that should be carried out in the conduct of such an experiment. 1

   (*c*) Why is avoidance of inbreeding likely to be favoured by natural selection? 2

   (*d*) Describe a different strategy for avoiding inbreeding that may be observed in polygamous social mammals, such as lions. 1

   (6)

2. Using examples, discuss the responses of intrinsically adaptable species to human activity. **(5)**

3. Each of the following titles refers to original research articles that have appeared in the journal *Animal Behaviour*.

   For each of the titles, explain the meaning of the term in **bold**.

   (*a*) "Fish cleaning symbiosis: **proximate causes** of host behaviour" 1

   (*b*) "Response **latency** as a function of the amount of reinforcement" 1

   (*c*) "Worker nutrition and **division of labour** in honey bees" 1

   (3)

[Turn over

ANIMAL BEHAVIOUR (continued)   *Marks*

4. Imprinting is an important process involved in a variety of different behaviours in many species.

   (a) (i)   Drugs that inhibit memory processes have been shown to disrupt imprinting. Explain how this supports the view that imprinting is a form of learning.   1

      (ii)   State **one** other feature of imprinting.   1

      (iii) Explain how imprinting can increase the protection of young members of a species.   1

   (b) In Paxton Lake, Canada, there are two species of three-spined sticklebacks (*Gasterosteus* spp.), illustrated below. An investigation was carried out to examine the possible role of imprinting in maintaining reproductive isolation in these species. In sticklebacks, males provide all of the parental care.

   Offspring were raised in three groups as follows:

      1   cross-fostered by father of the other species – "het" father

      2   fostered by father of the same species – "con" father

      3   no father.

   When sexually mature, female offspring of the three groups were scored for degree of preference for mates of either species ("het" or "con" mates). The results are shown in the graph below.

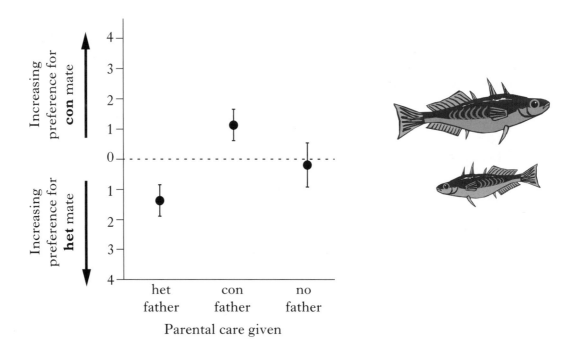

   (i)   What evidence is there that females in the "no father" group had no preference for species of mate?   1

   (ii) What do the results suggest about the mate preference of cross-fostered females?   1

   (iii) Stickleback males have an elaborate courtship display. Give one signal in the display that can stimulate a fixed action pattern.   1

    (6)

[End of *Animal Behaviour* questions. *Physiology, Health and Exercise* questions start on *Page twenty-five*]

Marks

SECTION C (continued)

PHYSIOLOGY, HEALTH AND EXERCISE

1. Discuss the importance of exercise in reducing the risk of cardiovascular disease.   **(5)**

2. (*a*)   (i)   What aspect of body composition is measured using bioelectrical impedance analysis (BIA)?   **1**

   (ii)   Give **one** limitation of BIA.   **1**

   (*b*)   The images below show sections of vertebrae from two females; one shows normal bone and one is from a female recently diagnosed with osteoporosis.

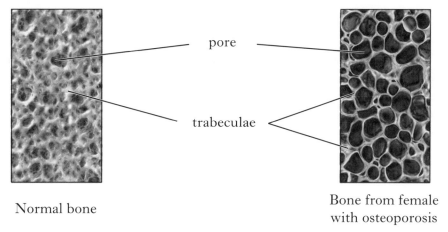

Normal bone   Bone from female
with osteoporosis

   (i)   With reference to the images above, describe the changes in bone structure as osteoporosis develops.   **1**

   (ii)   What action can be taken to delay the onset of osteoporosis?   **1**

   (iii)   Why does osteoporosis develop more quickly in females than in males?   **1**

   (5)

[Turn over

Marks

PHYSIOLOGY, HEALTH AND EXERCISE (continued)

3. The thermic effect of food (TE) is the energy expended in digesting and processing nutrients. Some substances in foods, however, can activate other processes that increase thermogenesis and thus influence total energy expenditure.

   (*a*) Total energy expenditure (EE) can be calculated using measured values in the following formula:

   $$EE = TE + \mathbf{A} + \mathbf{B}$$

   Identify components A and B.   1

   (*b*) Total energy expenditure can be determined in a laboratory using data recorded during respiratory gas analysis.

   (i) What **two** aspects of gas exchange must be measured during this analysis?   1

   (ii) Explain why this procedure is referred to as indirect calorimetry.   1

   (*c*) *Capsinoids*, a group of substances found in a type of red pepper, are known to increase energy expenditure through thermogenesis. A study examined the effect of capsinoids on energy expenditure in healthy adult males. Subjects were given capsules of capsinoid or placebo (no capsinoid).

   The graph below shows changes in total EE (ΔEE) for individuals following treatment.

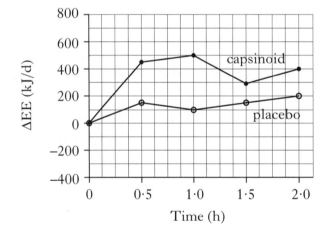

   (i) Calculate the thermogenic effect of the capsinoid at 1·0 h.   1

   (ii) The study used a 'single-blind' procedure. In this procedure, the subjects were not told which capsule they were receiving.

   Suggest how this aspect of the study improves its validity.   1

   (5)

Marks

PHYSIOLOGY, HEALTH AND EXERCISE (continued)

4. (a) Individuals with high VO_{2max} have greater aerobic fitness. VO_{2max} can be determined by maximal or sub-maximal testing.

    (i) What is meant by sub-maximal testing?   1

    (ii) In maximal testing, what **two** factors are measured to determine VO_{2max}?   1

(b) There is recent evidence that short periods of high-intensity training (HIT) can be used to help athletes reach peak aerobic fitness. In the study below, HIT involved six training sessions over two weeks. Each session consisted of ten repeats of cycling all-out for six seconds, with a one-minute rest between repeats.

Two teams of racing cyclists took part in the study; one group did the HIT training, the other followed its normal training routines.

The results of two tests are shown below. Figure 1 shows the time to exhaustion when participants performed a cycle test that gradually increases demand. Figure 2 shows the time taken to complete a 10 km cycling time trial.

Figure 1: Time to exhaustion   **Figure 2: Time for 10 km trial**

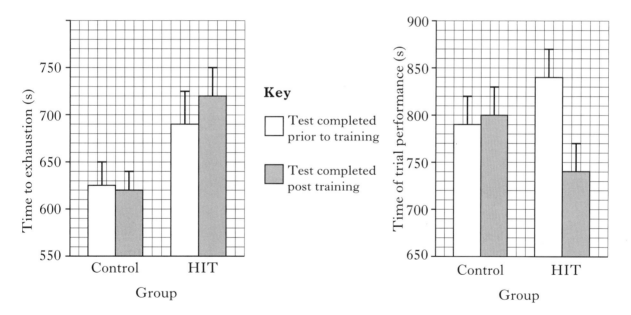

    (i) Refer to Figure 1. How does the evidence support the conclusions that:

      A: "Members of the HIT group were fitter than the control group" and

      B: "Members of the HIT group did not improve their VO_{2max}"?   2

    (ii) What evidence is there that HIT has improved performance?   1

                                                                      (5)

[END OF QUESTION PAPER]

SQA ADVANCED HIGHER
BIOLOGY 2010–2014

BIOLOGY ADVANCED HIGHER
2010

SECTION A

1.	C	**14.**	C
2.	D	**15.**	B
3.	C	**16.**	D
4.	A	**17.**	B
5.	A	**18.**	B
6.	C	**19.**	D
7.	B	**20.**	C
8.	C	**21.**	D
9.	A	**22.**	D
10.	B	**23.**	A
11.	D	**24.**	B
12.	D	**25.**	B
13.	A		

SECTION B

1. (a) it/oncogene is **dominant**
    the mutation/mutated allele is dominant
    mutated proto-oncogene/mutated proliferation gene are dominant

    (b) (i) monolayer/one layer/single layer
        confluent/**complete** coverage
    (ii) stimulates cell proliferation/division
        or
        provides/is a source of growth factors/MPF

    (c) (i) the two genes/*EML4* and *ALK* alone/not fused/do not transform cells/produce foci
    (ii) modification of fusion (gene) stops foci formation/transformation
        modification removes kinase activity

    (d) (At zero inhibitor conc. in Fig 2 and Fig 3)
        both normal and transformed cells start at 10^6 cells and both reach 10^{10} cells by day 7

    (e) (i) (at day 7, cell number) in absence of inhibitor is 10^{10} and 10^8 in presence of inhibitor **and** difference of $\times 10^2$
    (ii) *Any one from:*
        • as concentration of inhibitor increases, (rate of) growth/proliferation decreases
        • inhibitor reduces growth more in transformed cells than normal cells
        • both 5 µmol l^{-1} and 10 µmol l^{-1} inhibitor reduce cell **number** relative to 0 µmol l^{-1}
    (iii) comparison of final cell numbers **or** of numbers at a specified period/time from both graphs
    (f) *Any one from:*
        This is the concentration that:
        • made transformed cells decrease
        • was effective at killing transformed cells
        • reduced transformed cell number to 10^2
        • would reduce tumour size
        very little effect on normal cells

2. (a) peptidoglycan

    (b) (i) C1 (of NAM) bonded to C4 (of NAG)
        OH of C1 is above plane/ring/carbon
    (ii) hydrolysis

3. *Any five from:*
    1. protein that spans the membrane
    2. works against concentration gradient/by active transport
    3. ATP provides phosphate
    4. phosphate attaches to pump/protein/protein phosphorylated
    5. phosphorylation/dephosphorylation alters conformation/shape of protein **or** description
    6. different conformations have different affinity for sodium/potassium
    7. (3) sodium ions (pumped) out of cell and (2) potassium in

4. (a) contains foreign DNA **or** contains DNA from another **species**

    (b) *Agrobacterium (tumefaciens)*/*A. tumefaciens*

    (c) selects for plants/cells with the plasmid/resistance gene **or** is toxic to (plant) cells with no plasmid/resistance gene
        surviving (plant) cells now have the desirable/transgene sequence

    (d) bacterial toxin/Bt toxin/insecticide in tomato/other plants
        herbicide resistance added to in corn/maize/cotton/other plants
        beta carotene added to/in rice
        increased shelf life (flavr savr) tomato

5. (a) (In intraspecific, individuals are from the same species so) individuals have the same resource needs/niche
        or
        converse for interspecific

    (b) (i) B
    (ii) any competition is negative
        or
        presence of any competitor reduces time spent feeding/at flower
        or
        interspecific more intense than **intra**specific

    (c) butterfly has other food/nectar sources
        or
        brambles pollinated by other insects /nectar eaten by other insects
        or
        idea that relationship is not intimate/fixed/symbiotic

6. (a) herbivores eat plants **and** detritivores eat dead/waste material

    (b) (i) comparison of sample 1 and sample 4
        at week 6:
            Sample 1: 11-12 % loss (88% remaining)
            Sample 4: 90% loss   (10% remaining)
        or
        compare data from sample 1 and sample 4
        sample 1 has 85% left at 12 weeks and sample 4 reached 85% remaining by week 1 (roughly). So rate of decomposition is 12 times faster = > 7

        Single mark options
        If not comparing Samples 1 and 4 but data show >7
        or
        losses calculated for Samples other than 1 and 4

(ii) error bars/results overlap **and**

no difference in results for types of gut/amount of decomposition

or

no **significant** difference

or

wide error bars so results very variable/are less reliable

(iii) material has been through two animal guts

and

idea that fragmentation/surface area increasing (so this sample has the highest rate of decomposition)

7. (a) with pollution there are favoured and susceptible species

indicator species defined as those that experience consequences/are sensitive to a pollutant

or

example showing **how** a favoured/susceptible species indicates pollution

(b) (i) 11 000 000

(ii) not enough time for diclofenac to reach safe levels or equivalent

8. **A** (i) *Any seven from:*

1. yield reduced by competition/disease/damage/herbivores
2. (any of above) controlled by reducing populations (to maximise food production)
3. weeds are competitors for the crop's resources
4. herbicides used to kill other plants/weeds
5. alternative methods of reducing weeds, e.g. hoeing, interplanting, (herbicide-tolerant) transgenics
6. more resources for the crop (increases yield)

   or e.g. of resource – nitrate, light, space
7. insects (damage crops by) eating plant parts
8. insecticides reduce insect populations/kill insects

   or (Bt) transgenic **or** biological control **or** barrier
9. herbivores removed or kept out (e.g. scarers, netting, fencing)
10. parasites/fungi/viruses reduce yield by causing disease
11. fungicides prevent/kill fungi
12. example of ecological impact of these activities

(ii) *Any eight from:*

13. cultivation of one species/crop (to exclusion of others)
14. to meet the demand/needs of increasing population
15. removal of hedgerows allows increased field size
16. reduces species diversity (e.g. predators)
17. reduces stability of ecosystem

    or increases susceptibility to pathogens
18. mechanisation increases efficiency of cropping/planting
19. reduce food costs/increases profit
20. may damage soil structure/increase compaction

    or may have negative impact on soil condition
21. cultivation of single species depletes particular nutrients
22. need for fertiliser/use of inorganic fertiliser (improves yield)
23. but can cause knock on pollution problems/eg of effect

8. **B** (i) *Any five from:*

1. energy fixed/light to chemical in photosynthesis
2. (photosynthesis carried out) by autotrophs/producers
3. productivity is **rate** of accumulation of biomass

   or productivity is mass units per area per time
4. primary productivity supports higher trophic levels

5. GPP is total yield of organic matter / total energy fixed
6. NPP is biomass remaining after producer respiration

   or equation
7. appropriate management/choice of biomass crop
8. explanation of role of biomass in the energy debate

   or relevant comment about 'carbon footprint'/neutrality

(ii) *Any ten from:*

9. fossil fuels are finite/non-renewable (energy) resources
10. need to be conserved
11. biofuels are alternative sources of energy
12. fossil fuels are **burned**
13. gases released SO_2/ NOx/ CO_2
14. these cause acid rain
15. effect of acid rain in ecosystems (e.g. forest damage, pH in lakes, etc)
16. CO_2 (from combustion) **enhances** greenhouse effect
17. cause global warming/climate change
18. changes abundance or distribution of species (general point)

    or example **other than** zooxanthellae
19. zooxanthellae and polyps/coral are symbiotic/mutualistic
20. and coral bleaching link to temperature rise
21. methane and CFCs other important greenhouse gases not from fossil fuels

SECTION C: BIOTECHNOLOGY

1. (a) (i) nif/nitrogen-fixing genes

   (ii) nitrogen converted to ammonia/ammonium

   (b) *Any two from:*

   nitrogenase activity declines with length of treatment

   no significant difference between 10 and 20 days

   there is a (significant) decrease in activity from 20 to 30 days

2. **Response to antigens**

1. antigens are recognised by B-lymphocytes

   or antigens activate B-lymphocytes
2. multiplication (of B-lymphocytes) in spleen/immune system
3. antibodies are produced
4. antibody binds/forms complex with antigen

   or antibodies are specific

Application

5. (highly purified) antigen injected into animal
6. bleeding of animal

   or red blood cells removed from blood sample
7. reinjection (with antigen) increases response
8. polyclonal serum produced **or** antibodies prepared from serum

3. (a) *Any one from:*

   Uniformity in terms of:
   - clones/genetic
   - growth rate
   - ripening
   - harvesting time
   - yields
   - taste

   high yielding disease free/virus free/economical

   (b) light intensity/temperature/humidity/nutrients/pH/water content

(c) (i) treatments are an improvement on the control **or** example

or

as concentration of regulators increase the explants increase

(ii) (At 0·5 IAA + 5·0 kinetin)

$58 \times 28 = 1624$ shoots = highest yield

4. (a) competition with gut pathogens **or** control pathogens **or** reduce diarrhoea

anti-cancer activity

reduction of blood cholesterol

reduced lactose intolerance

(b) (i) direct count would include living and dead

or dilution plating gives viable count

or alternative comparisons, eg **live** bacteria needed so need **viable** count

(ii) prevent contamination/maintain aseptic technique

(iii) only count between 30 and 300

or

enough to be accurate and not too many to count

(iv) correct value 6×10^{10}

plate to bottle $4 = 6 \times 10^3$

dilution factor from bottle 1 to bottle $4 = \mathbf{10^4}$
$(10^2 \times 10 \times 10)$

scaling $0 \cdot 1$ cm^3 sample from 100 cm^3 in carton $= 10^3$

Plate ──────────> bottles ──────────> carton
60 in 0.1 × 100 = 6000   ×10 ×10 ×100   ×1000

SECTION C: ANIMAL BEHAVIOUR

1. (a) background/height/tree species/type of woodland etc

(b) B or E

(c) (B was expected to give best survival but)

Little difference between B and C

or C is effective yet has only one spot/has 'no eyes'

(E with two 'eyes' was expected to give high survival but)

Increase in number of spots increases survival

F–E–D (24/48 hrs)

(A, the control has no contrast and)

In all treatments survival is higher than control

B–C–D have highest contrast and highest survival

Appropriate quantification

(d) mimicry/batesian mimicry/mullerian mimicry

crypsis/camouflage

masquerade

disruptive coloration

aposematic/warning coloration

2. *Any four from:*

1. hierarchy is system of (social) ranking
2. established by fighting/maintained by threat or ritualised display
3. reduced aggression/fighting (once established)
4. increased protection/better chance of survival
5. co-operative hunting/all group members get food
6. division of labour/opportunities for learning

3. (a) ethogram

(b) (i) sexual dimorphism

(ii) to attract females/to permit female choice/to elicit response from females

(c) (i) brother-sister matings

or

mating (only) between closely related fish

or Prevent dispersal/keep all family individuals in the same area

(ii) reduces breeding success **or** less fertilisation and less hatching

Inbreeding causes:

increased expression of disadvantageous/lethal/recessive genes

increased homozygosity/inbreeding depression

4. (a) (i) high-learning flies die younger/shorter life span

(ii) (on average/in either group) females live longer than males

or

greater reduction in life span/longevity for females (in high-learning group)

(iii) much longer life span in primates

or

learning has bigger role in primate behaviour

or

learning benefits outweigh the costs in primates

(b) *Any two from:*

irreversible/difficult to reverse

environmental component/object in environment

critical time period (after hatching/birth)

object (of attachment) followed to exclusion of others

SECTION C: PHYSIOLOGY, HEALTH AND EXERCISE

1. (a) *Any two from:*

3+ hours/endurance level of exercise results in lower (resting) heart/pulse rate than **the others**

3+ hours/endurance level of exercise results in greater left ventricle mass than **the others**

athletic heart defined as increased LV thickness **and** increased SV/lower (resting) pulse

(b) stroke volume

(c) increased LV mass

(d) less plaque/atheroma build up/atherosclerosis

better lipid profile/higher HDL:LDL ratio/higher HDL/lower LDL

better myocardial circulation

lower (resting) BP

lowers risk of MI/stroke

2. *Any five from:*

1. pancreas senses glucose (in blood)
2. insulin secretion/production (increases) when glucose is high
3. insulin increases glucose uptake by liver/muscle/cells
4. insulin **promotes** glycogen synthesis/conversion of glucose to glycogen
5. insulin increases the number of glucose transporters (in cell membranes)
6. obesity leads to/is a risk factor for NIDDM (Type 2 diabetes)
7. obesity/NIDDM leads to insulin resistance/loss of sensitivity to insulin/fewer **active** receptors
8. reduced entry of glucose into cells
9. (in NIDDM) insulin concentration initially increases

3. (a) bone mass/density is increasing in this period

or

to increase bone density (before age-related loss)

or

weight bearing activity is likely to be high

(b) reference to menopause around this age/oestrogen starts to decline/women start to lose bone mass rapidly/when osteoporosis (most likely) starts

may counteract/slow down (age-related/oestrogen-related) losses

or

maintain bone density/mass
or
delay onset of osteoporosis

4. (a) (i) measures heat output/loss

in **insulated** chamber/environment
or measure energy required to keep chamber
temperature constant

(ii) volume of air breathed
% oxygen breathed in and % of oxygen in air out
or difference in percentages

(b) (i) 838.3 kJ

(ii) select foods with biggest deviation from
20·20 kJ (starch or protein)

correct calculation of either extreme (as fraction of
single food value)

starch (low) = 4·62%   protein (high) = 4·87%

or

5% limits from 20.20 are 19·19 kJ to 21·21 kJ
and
conclude all four are in range

or

4 deviations calculated correctly
and
conclude all four are in range

BIOLOGY ADVANCED HIGHER 2011

SECTION A

1.	C	14.	A
2.	B	15.	A
3.	B	16.	C
4.	D	17.	C
5.	D	18.	D
6.	B	19.	C
7.	A	20.	D
8.	A	21.	C
9.	B	22.	B
10.	D	23.	D
11.	D	24.	B
12.	A	25.	B
13.	C		

SECTION B

1. (a) (i) *Any two from:*
Type of symbiosis **or** idea of close/intimate association
between two **species**
<u>Host</u> harmed and <u>parasite</u> benefits
Benefit (to parasite) in terms of nutrition/energy/
resources

(ii) Obligate

(b) (i) Idea of checking human faeces (for parasite eggs)

(ii) *Any two from:*
Health education/ideas on how to reduce infection
Sanitation/prevent faeces reaching lake
Drug treatment (for superspreaders)

(c) (i) Intervention village(s) reach target/1% and control(s)
don't.
Use data to illustrate trends

(ii) Commit to position about the results (reliable or
unreliable) **and** justify appropriately, eg 'Reliable
because two villages used for treatment and control', or
'not reliable because (*only*) *two* villages …' Reliability
in relation to **error bars** – when error bars are small
the reliability is better

(d) (i) Difficult to kill them all
or
Survivors reproduce rapidly

(ii) *Any one from:*
(Parasites still exist as)
Adults long lived/still inside host
Eggs still being produced
Free-living parasite stages not affected

(e) *S.japonicum* can infect other **mammals**/can have a range
of primary hosts
(so) cattle have to be kept away from lake
(and) mice can be used for test purposes

2. (a) photosynthesis **and** respiration

(b) 12.5%

(c) (i) added to by human activity
(ii) methane/CFC/nitrous oxide/ozone

3. (a) (i) earlier species **change conditions/environment** to
better suit later species
(ii) allogenic

(b) (i) bioaccumulation/bioconcentration
(ii) high toxicity so herbivores/primary consumers die
or

biomagnification makes herbivores too toxic (for carnivores)/biomagnification results in toxicity in higher trophic levels

or

low productivity/too little energy to support higher levels

(iii) survives high conc. of nickel while **other species** susceptible

or

the **relative abundance** depends on Ni levels of soil

4. *Any four from:*
    1. Fundamental niche is the resources a species is capable of using/could use in the absence of competition
    2. Realised niche is the resources a species actually uses or available in presence of competitors
    3. (Competition arises) when resources limited
    4. Competitive exclusion arises from interspecific competition/when two **species** competing
    5. Two **species** with the same/similar niche cannot coexist (in same location)
    6. (One species will survive and) one species will die out/local extinction

5. (a) (i) (For the increase in O_2 pressure 0–30 units)
            Myoglobin increases to 0.975
            Haemoglobin increases to 0.50
       (ii) curves differ/binding differs
            tertiary (structure) the same/similar
            only Hb has quaternary

    (b) 1 (less)

    (c) prosthetic groups

6. (a) (i) hydrophilic/not lipid soluble
       (ii) (signal) transduction

    (b) (i) at most/all GABA concentrations more chloride movement (with drug present)
       (ii) change in conformation/shape (of the GABA receptor)

7. (a) single-stranded DNA
        (bases) complementary **or** strand anneals (to template)

    (b) *Any one from:*
        (gene) probes/probing
        (gel) electrophoresis
        blotting
        sequencing
        restriction digest

    (c) (Test is negative for ΔF508 so counselling needs to warn of) other possible mutations (30%) causing CF
        or low chance of having/carrying CF

8. A (i) *Any five from:*
        Prokaryotic DNA
        1. within cytoplasm/not contained in a nuclear membrane
        2. exists as a circular DNA molecule/nucleoid
        3. plasmids are **additional** circles/rings of DNA
        Eukaryotic
        4. contained within a nuclear membrane
        5. DNA is associated with histone/proteins
        6. organised as nucleosomes/chromatin
        7. (nucleosomes) coiled/condensed to form chromosomes
        8. chromosomes are linear

      (ii) *Any ten from:*
        Prokaryotic
        9. ribosomes (only organelle)
        10. cell wall made of peptidoglycan
        11. capsule/layer of mucus (lipopolysaccharide) is protective/is adhesive

12. pili for cell attachment/exchanging plasmids
13. flagella for movement
    Eukaryotic
14. name and function of one organelle from list below
15. name and function of another organelle from list below
16. cytoskeleton is a system of protein fibres that provide support **or** movement **or** movement/organisation of organelles
17. animal cells (may) have microvilli to increase surface area/absorption
18. plant cell walls made of cellulose
19. middle lamella is where plant cell walls contact (rich in pectin)
20. plasmodesmata connect cytoplasms/adjacent plant cells
21. plant cells (may) also contain – chloroplasts for photosynthesis **or** vacuoles for cell sap

8. B **Eukaryotic**
    Endoplasmic reticulum – transport of proteins/synthesis of lipids
    Golgi apparatus – processing/modification/secretion of proteins
    Mitochondrion – (aerobic) respiration/ATP production
    Lysosomes – enzymatic digestion
    Microbodies/peroxisomes – oxidation reactions
    Ribosomes – protein synthesis
    Nucleolus – ribosome formation

    (i) *Any five from:*
        1. interphase is G_1, S, G_2
           or interphase is the period between cell divisions
        2. G_1 and G_2 are growth periods **or** organelles/ proteins made
        3. DNA replication occurs during S phase
        4. G_1 checkpoint assesses cell size/mass
        5. G_1 checkpoint ensures there is sufficient (mass) to make two daughter cells/to enter S phase
        6. G_2 checkpoint assesses DNA replication
        7. G_2 checkpoint controls entry into mitosis
        8. ensuring each daughter cell receives a complete genome/'set' of DNA

    (ii) *Any five from:*
        9. spindle fibres are microtubules
        10. correct description of one phase of mitosis – as in notes
        11. as above
        12. M/metaphase checkpoint controls entry to **anaphase**
        13. ensures chromosomes are aligned correctly (on the equator)
            or ensures each daughter cell receives correct number of chromosomes/chromatids
        14. mitosis promoting factor (MPF) needed for entry to mitosis
            or MPF is a protein
        15. cytokinesis is the division of the cytoplasm/separation into two cells

    (iii) *Any five from:*
        16. proto-oncogenes/proliferation genes stimulate cell division
        17. proto-oncogenes mutate to oncogenes
        18. oncogenes stimulate excessive/abnormal cell division/tumour formation
        19. tumour suppressor genes/anti-proliferation genes inhibit cell division
        20. tumour suppressors act at checkpoints
        21. (tumour suppressor) mutation results in loss of inhibition/loss of control of division

22. oncogenes are dominant and in tumour suppressor genes, mutations are recessive

or

only single oncogene mutation required whereas two tumour suppressor mutations required

SECTION C: BIOTECHNOLOGY

1. (a) Antibiotic **and** type of organism
   e.g. penicillin and *Penicillium*/fungus

   or

   Correct antibiotic and *Streptomyces*/bacterium

   (b) (i) So that only a single species/strain is used to prepare the inoculums
       or idea of pure culture
       or uncontaminated culture

   (ii) Area X

   (c) dissolve oxygen/aerate
       or to achieve distribution of nutrients/fungal cells/heat energy/efficient mixing

   (d) *Any one from:*
       filtration/ultrafiltration
       addition of salt to a penicillin rich solvent
       precipitation from solvent/flocculation
       centrifugation
       crystallisation

   (e) production starts as glucose is (nearly) exhausted
       or lag period 0-1.5 days before production begins

       production begins towards end of active growth/exponential phase
       or production begins as stationary phase is entered/growth plateaus

2. (a) *Any two from:*
   Mouse injected with antigens
   Production of B-cells triggered/activated
   (B-cells) isolated from spleen

   (b) Polyethylene glycol/PEG

   (c) *Any one from:*
   • mAbs bind to cancer cell-specific antigens
   • immune response against target cancer cell triggered
     or body destroys its own cancer cells
   • delivery of radiation directly to tumours (radioactive molecule can be attached to mAb)
   • delivery of attached toxin to destroy cancer cell
   • treatment of breast cancer using herceptin
   • mAb can prevent growth of cancer cells (by blocking growth receptors)

3. 1. cell walls reduce yield
   2. composition/component: pectin, cellulose, araban
   3. cellulose tough/causes difficulty with breaking open cells
      or cellulose makes mechanical extraction difficult
   4. pectin increases viscosity/causes difficulty with filtration
   5. pectin/araban cause haze/cloudiness
   6. first example of enzyme used to break down the wall materials (see list below)
   7. second example (see list below)
   8. low solubility issues of araban and pectin

   Examples
   Cellulose breaks down cellulose/increases yield
   Pectinase breaks down pectin/decreases viscosity/decreases haze
   Arabanase breaks down araban/decreases haze

4. (a) Living cells only

   (b) (i) 1.25% and 2.5%
       (ii) same initial concentration of colony forming units/same viable count added to each dilution
       (iii) 9 million cells

SECTION C: ANIMAL BEHAVIOUR

1. (a) (i) 15
       (ii) *Any one from:*
           they break more easily/less (total) height needed to break them
           it takes fewer drops to break them
           shorter handling time
           less time/energy to break shells

   (b) optimal foraging maximises net energy gain

       it gives the lowest **total** height needed to break a whelk
       the least energy expenditure in flight at this height

       or

   (c) Encounter rate (of prey by predator)/search time

2. 1. nature = behaviour that is innate/instinct/genetically determined
      or
      nature allows stereotyped response to stimuli
   2. nurture defined as behavioural modification/learning
   3. nature eg: any example of instinctive behaviour
   4. nurture eg: imprinting/habituation/cultural transmission
      or description of species and behaviour
   5. (adult) invertebrates generally have a shorter **lifespan** than primates *
   6. long lifespan gives time for learning
   7. short lifespan entails reliance on innate behaviour
      or
      invertebrates rely on innate behaviour
   8. invertebrate **parental care** is rare *
   9. primates rely more on **nurture than do invertebrates**
   * converse applies

3. (a) (i) *Any two from:*
           Healthy females produce many eggs
           Brood pouch filled faster/reduced mating time
           Reduced predation risks
           Increase in number of eggs fertilised
       (ii) *Any one from:*
           Genes allow more copies to pass into next generation
           Genes more likely to be passed on to next generation
           Genes are self-preserving
           Genes assist survival of the male fish

   (b) *Any one from:*
       Nutrition of young in brood pouch/carrying young
       Providing parental care

   (c) Males do not avoid other males with black spots

   (d) Fish with solvent only

   (e) Males are not influenced by displays/stimuli that females might show if they saw the males

4. (a) (On average) they share half of their genes/genetic material
       or The chances of sharing a gene are 0.5/50%

   (b) (i) Genes for altruism will spread when rB−C>0
           or
           helping relatives is beneficial when rB−C>0
       (ii) (Three) groups of most related have highest cannibalism
           or
           no correlation

SECTION C: PHYSIOLOGY, HEALTH AND EXERCISE

1. 1. deposition of fatty materials/plaque forms/atheroma forms
   2. (atheroma) **under** lining layer/endothelium/intima **of artery**
   3. platelets attach to rough surface/platelets release clotting factors
      or thrombus/clot forms at site of plaque
   4. clot/embolus/atheroma can block/narrow vessel
   5. **blockage** of <u>coronary artery</u>
   6. heart muscle cells **die** beyond blockage
      or heart muscle cells **die** from lack of oxygen

2. (*a*) **increase** exercise
       reduce intake of fatty foods

   (*b*) (i) <u>5.9</u> (mmol/l)
       (ii) *Any two from:*
            LDL has been reduced (to 2.9)/LDL now within normal range
            Total cholesterol is reduced/now about normal
            Total cholesterol/HDL ratio reduced/now about normal
       (iii) 32.7% **or** (about) 33%

3. (*a*) pancreas/islets/Beta cells **detect** glucose **and** insulin secretion (increases)

       (Glucose level is reduced when)
       cells in liver/muscle/adipose tissue (increase) uptake glucose
       or
       glucose is converted to/stored as glycogen

   (*b*) (i) fewer receptors active/functioning/responding to insulin
            or
            receptors do not recruit glucose transporters to the membrane
       (ii) obesity is cause (of insulin resistance/Type 2 diabetes)

            high W:H/this ratio is an indicator for obesity (so worth reducing it)
            or
            (reducing ratio) will reduce obesity/BMI

4. (*a*) (Sporting activities) increase bone mass/bone density/bone mineral density (BMD)
       or
       osteoporosis takes longer to develop because BMD is higher

       greatest bone mass achieved when young/by age of 30/in adolescence
       or
       gives higher BMD before age-related loss

   (*b*) (i) These are most common fracture sites in elderly/those with osteoporosis
       (ii) not a weight bearing exercise and allows comparison with the others
            or
            to demonstrate that **only** weight bearing exercise is effective
       (iii) (Sample data eg)
            size of sample, replication
            variation in BMD/age between subjects
            idea of measuring error, eg error bars

SECTION A

1.	B	14.	A
2.	D	15.	B
3.	D	16.	A
4.	B	17.	B
5.	D	18.	C
6.	C	19.	D
7.	A	20.	C
8.	C	21.	B
9.	A	22.	D
10.	B	23.	A
11.	C	24.	C
12.	D	25.	A
13.	C		

SECTION B

1. (*a*) (i) phosphodiester (bonds)/phosphoester
       (ii) (complementary) base pairing **and**
            stops the shape unravelling/creates the shape/holds shape

   (*b*) *Any two from:*
       Drosha not working
       miRNA/precursor not processed/cut
       no (micro)RNA strand for RISC
       or RISC can't bind (m)RNA
       (RNA) interference reduced/translation is left on

   (*c*) (i) <u>62.5</u>
       (ii) more KO cells in G1 **and** fewer in S (and G2+M)
            differences are significant (only) in G1 and S/error bars don't overlap in G1 and S
            or if comparing only G1 bars or only S bars, then must point out significant difference (for 1 mark)

   (*d*) (i) *Any two from:*
            • in KO cells it is (generally) lower than normal cells
            • it increases in normal cells (over time)
            • in KO cells **and** one from below
                 no trend
                 decreases from day 8
                 increases (to day 8) then decreases
       (ii) in normal cells, as differentiation increases self-renewal decreases
            or converse
            Any one from:
            in KO/abnormal cells, **both** processes decrease after day 8
            or
            in KO/abnormal cells, **both** processes increase to day 8
            or
            in KO abnormal cells, self-renewal remains higher and differentiation remains lower **than normal**

   (*e*) lactose absent
       repressor binds to operator

2. (*a*) (i) binding is extracellular/to cell surface/to membrane
            change in cAMP is inside the cell / intracellular
            or
            change in intracellular signal molecule/second messenger
       (ii) crypsis/camouflage/description of camouflage

(b) (i) (mechanical) support/strength/shape
cell movement
spindle fibres/separation of chromatids/movement of chromosomes

  (ii) tubulin

  (iii) centrosome/centriole/MTOC

3. *Any five from:*
1. inhibitors reduce enzyme activity
2. competitive inhibitors resemble substrate
3. (CI) binds to/occupies active site **and** prevents substrate access
4. non-competitive inhibitors/negative modulators bind at a second site/allosteric site
5. non CI/negative modulator alters the shape of the **active site**
6. substrate binding reduced/prevented
7. idea of modulation (of rate) by change in **affinity** of active site for substrate
8. allosteric enzymes involved in regulation of pathways

4. (a) probe

(b) Yes. fragment from P is shorter because of the deletion
shorter fragment goes further (in the gel)
or
DNA with deletion goes further (in the gel)

(c) polymerase chain reaction/PCR

5. (a) bioaccumulation

(b) (i) 30% (or 29.64 or 29.6)
  (ii) run-off from land/leaching/spray **and** reaches **sea** through food chain/biomagnifications

6. (a) **energy loss** (from food chain) **and** via:
high metabolic rate/homeothermy/heat/respiration/movement
herbivory/food source high in cellulose/uneaten parts/undigested parts

(b) (i) less predation **or** more feeding
  (ii) (further global warming because)
shorter winter ice duration reduces krill population density
so less faeces to trap carbon (dioxide) from the atmosphere
or
faeces (now) decompose **or** decomposition begins
carbon dioxide returned to atmosphere

7. (a) suspended growth/suspended development/suspended life cycle/**reduced** metabolism

(b) (large fields have) fewer hedges/fewer rose plants **so** fewer insects/disrupts life-cycle
(increased yield from) less feeding/less disease

(c) organism/species that transfers **parasite** between **hosts**

8. A
1. definition of niche: (multi-dimensional summary of) resources/requirements of species
2. fundamental niche is the resources a species is **capable** of using/could use
3. realised niche is the resources a species actually uses **or** are available in presence of competitors
4. competition defined as two organisms attempting to utilise same resource
5. (competition arises) when resources limited
6. competition is negative for both species
or
competition is a negative-negative/(−/−) interaction
7. example of negative outcome/cost (reduced growth, fecundity, population decrease, increased mortality)
8. intraspecific same species and interspecific different species
9. intraspecific competition more intense (than interspecific)
10. because all require same/similar resources
11. exploitation competition defined as use of resource reducing the supply to others
12. interference competition is when access to resource is prevented
13. example of either of above
14. two **species** with the same/similar niche cannot coexist (in same location)
15. competitive exclusion arises from interspecific competition/when two **species** competing
16. (one species will survive and) one species will die out/local extinction
17. resource partitioning allows exploitation/sharing of different components of a resource
18. resource partitioning reduces competition
19. example of resource partitioning
20. definition of exotic species as introduced /alien
21. invasive in terms of better competitor/ lacking predators/ lacking herbivores/lacking parasites
22. example of ecological damage caused by named invasive species

8. B (i) **Decomposition**
1. decomposition is break down of organic matter to inorganic
or decomposition is mineralisation
2. soil organisms particularly important
3. detritivores are invertebrates/**or** example
4. ...that produce humus/that fragment detritus/wastes
5. increases surface area so speeds up decomposition
6. enzymes/digestion internal (in detritivores)
7. decomposers are bacteria and fungi
8. enzymes / digestion external (from decomposers)
9. decomposer respiration is final releaser of CO_2
10. decomposition limited by available nitrogen

(ii) **Nutrient cycling**
A maximum of ten from:
11. finite supply of nutrients
12. cycles maintain the supply
13. uptake/fixation by plants
14. *Any two from:* assimilation, transformation, food chains, and decomposition
15. loss of nutrient from ecosystem eg. via leaching
16. low solubility of P limits phosphorus cycle
17. decomposition of (organic) N compounds produces ammonium
or decomposition is called ammonification
18. nitrification is ammonium to nitrite to nitrate
19. *Nitrosomonas* converts ammonium to nitrite
20. *Nitrobacter* converts nitrite to nitrate
21. denitrification is nitrate to N gas
22. anaerobic / occurs rapidly in waterlogged soil
23. N fixation: nitrogen gas converted to ammonium
24. Cyanobacteria (N fixers) are free-living/in soil/in water
25. *Rhizobium* in root nodules / legumes
26. nitrogenase (that does the N fixing) is inhibited by oxygen
27. leghaemoglobin in nodule reduces oxygen level

SECTION C: BIOTECHNOLOGY

1. (a) spleen

(b) to make the cell line immortal/so that fused cells can divide indefinitely/because myeloma cells are immortal

(c) (i) the medium kills them

(ii) (unfused lymphocytes) divide a number of times and die/are not immortal/have a limited lifespan

(d) 1st step selects for desired antibody
2nd step: selection of the cell that makes the (desired) antibody

2. *Any five from:*
   1. plot growth curve/obtain values of cell numbers over specified time period
   2. to identify exponential phase
   3. use exponential phase to calculate g
   4. g = time for population to double/time for one division
   5. growth rate constant (k) = ln2/g
   6. k is number of doublings/generations per unit time
   7. k is used to optimise growing conditions
   8. to maximise enzyme production

3. (a) (i) cellulase/pectinase
   (ii) improves clarity/reduces haze/breaks down hemicellulose/removes araban

   (b) (i) (affinity) chromatography
   (ii) the **shape** of the enzyme/active site is specific to (the shape of) the substrate

4. (a) kills (the majority of the) naturally occurring **bacteria**/spoilage **bacteria**/harmful **bacteria**/pathogens

   (b) (i) lactose to lactic acid
   (ii) generates flavour/texture

   (c) (i) 10×10^7 **or** 10^8
   (ii) mixed culture grew to 9×10^7, pure to 3×10^7
   or other correct quantification

SECTION C: ANIMAL BEHAVIOUR

1. (a) head up/scanning/not drinking or eating

   (b) (i) randomly selected individuals
   focal sampling (for eg 5 mins)/other sampling strategies
   ethogram/check list
   avoid influence by observer/use camouflage, hide etc.
   video recording/use of camera/ remote telemetry

   (ii) *Any two from:*
   vigilance does decrease as group size increases when lions are present (but)
   when lions are absent the vigilance is not related to group size
   lions increase vigilance in smaller groups sizes but not larger (beyond 11)

   (iii) lions present graph depends on one sample of group size 16
   or
   some group sizes have no values (8,9,10,13,14,15)
   or
   some group sizes have only 1 sample (6,7,16)
   or
   some group sizes have large variation in replicates (3,4)

2. (a) as body size increases so does crater diameter/size

   (b) (i) individually characteristic/highly repeatable/outside body/innate/gene expression determines outward behaviour

   (ii) any built structure; eg nests/homes/traps etc
   or
   behaviours such as herding/shoaling/bird song

   (c) crater building/coloration/display behaviour

3. (a) (i) younger subordinates groomed more frequently
   or
   as age of subordinate increases, grooming decreases
   (ii) duration/intensity

(b) *Any two from:*
reinforce close relationships or alliances/develop bonds/lower dominance threat/maintain social rank/hygiene/courtship

(c) "... **not necessarily closely related** to the young animals that they help to rear."
they are not assisting the survival of their own genes
or
altruism generally involves kin selection/close relatives (and this isn't)

4. *Any five from:*
   1. sign stimuli/releasers are signals that elicit **specific** response
   2. FAP is automatic/stereotyped/species specific response
   3. (FAPs are) under genetic control/innate
   4. (FAPs are) resistant to change (by learning)
      or once initiated go to completion
   5. series of releasers/FAPs can produce complex behaviour
   6. (herring) gull adult has red spot on bill (releaser)
   7. elicits (FAP of) chick pecking at spot
   8. (then releases) parent provides food

SECTION C: PHYSIOLOGY, HEALTH AND EXERCISE

1. (a) systolic = 120 and diastolic = 70
   or
   systolic/diastolic
   or
   systolic and diastolic pressures in mmHg

   (b) narrowing/obstruction/loss of elasticity increases resistance
   or
   force on artery wall increases pressure
   or
   to keep the same flow (rate) the BP goes up

   (c) (i) 40.7%
   (ii) (with exertion) heart's demand for oxygen increases/heart rate increases
   but
   diastole shorter
   or time for O_2 delivery shorter
   or lower coronary circulation/oxygen to cardiac muscles

   (d) 5 **or** 10mg **significantly** better than control

2. (a) not obese. BMI = 27 **and** less than 30/obesity cut-off

   (b) (i) mass and volume
   (ii) used in (Siri) equation **or** (495/density) – 450

   (c) underestimates fat

3. (a) *Any one from:*
   improve increase HDL:LDL
   improve/increase HDL
   reduces LDL / reduces triglycerides / reduces cholesterol

   (b) *Any two from:*
   increases glucose uptake (in muscle and fat cells)
   increases number of **active** receptors
   increases number of glucose transporters (in target cells)
   increases (enzymes for) glycogen synthesis

   (c) starting/fasting insulin concentration is reduced by exercise
   and correct quantification
   or
   starting/fasting insulin concentration is reduced equally at both exercise levels
   and correct quantification
   or (in response to same food intake)
   both exercise levels result in lower insulin production than control
   and correct quantification
   or

insulin increases less after exercise
and correct quantification
or
as the level of exercise increased the insulin response to the meal decreased
and correct quantification

4. *Any four from:*
   1. individual overweight because energy in > energy out
   2. exercise increases energy out/gives negative energy balance
   3. exercise leads to weight loss/fat loss
   4. exercise (may not alter weight) may increase muscle/alter balance between muscle and fat
   5. BMR increase causes increased energy output
      or
      more lean tissue so higher BMR
   6. the effect of exercise on body mass may decrease as fat decreases
   7. reference to exercise programme: (*any one from*) frequency, duration, intensity and type of exercise

BIOLOGY ADVANCED HIGHER 2013

SECTION A

1.	A	**14.**	A
2.	C	**15.**	B
3.	D	**16.**	D
4.	B	**17.**	A
5.	B	**18.**	C
6.	A	**19.**	A
7.	B	**20.**	D
8.	A	**21.**	C
9.	C	**22.**	D
10.	C	**23.**	B
11.	C	**24.**	B
12.	D	**25.**	D
13.	D		

SECTION B

1. (*a*) (i) Introduced (by human activity / artificially) alien / foreign / not native / not naturally in North America

   (ii) Reduces (populations of) other species
   or
   can cause extinction of other species
   or
   lowers diversity

   (*b*) (i) Population of both species higher when separate / in Exp A
   or
   equivalent for Exp B
   D.lum 25 vs 11 **or** *D.pul* 37 vs 22.

   (ii) competitive exclusion (principle)
   or
   (local) extinction

   (iii) *Any one from:*
   In Exp C / predators present
   D. lumholtzi > *D pulicaria*

   D lum decreases in Exp B / no predators but increases in Exp C / predators present

   D. pulicaria decreased in the presence of predators but not in their absence

   (*c*) (i) Increase in length of tail spine

   (ii) To allow comparison of (fleas with) different body size.

   (iii) 0·4 mm

   (iv) *Any two from:*
   In both species tail spines increase
   D.lum tail spines increase more than *D.pul* (tail) spines
   Head spines only increase in *D.lum* (decrease in *D.pul*)

   (*d*) *Any two from:*
   crypsis / camouflage / masquerade / disruptive coloration / warning (aposematic) coloration / mimicry

2. *Any five from:*

   1. Autotrophs fix light (energy) into chemicals / biomass / GPP

   2. Heterotrophs obtain energy from food / from NPP
      or
      Energy is transferred from one trophic level to another by feeding

   3. Energy losses occur at a trophic level / at transfers

   4. Ecological efficiency as percentage transferred

5. Energy lost in excreted / egested / uneaten material

6. Energy flow to detritivores / decomposers / saprotrophs

7. All energy ultimately lost as heat
   or
   Heat energy lost from respiration

3. (*a*) Climax (community)

   (*b*) Increased and *any one from*:
   food web complexity
   species diversity / biodiversity / plant diversity
   nutrient levels in soil / humus
   variety of habitats
   variety / number of niches

   (*c*) (i) Production of toxic compounds
        or
        shading (neighbouring) plants / heather

        (ii) Underground stems allow bracken to grow back / re-establish

        (iii) low specificity / kills other species / reduces diversity
        or
        persistence leads to (unexpected) toxic effects

4. (*a*) *Any two from:*
   Regulation has energy costs

   Oxygen consumption is higher at lower salinities / as salinity increases oxygen consumption decreases (to 2.5%)

   Greater oxygen use reflects greater energy demand / ATP production (to maintain internal conditions)

   (*b*) (i) Osmoconformer

        (ii) as (sea) salinity rises, internal ion levels increase and body fluids / tissues / the animal can resist freezing

   (*c*) Restricted / limited / narrower (range)

5. (*a*) *Any one from:*
   Reference to (membrane) fluidity
   Reference to permeability
   stabilises (membranes)
   Prevents crystallisation (of membrane)

   (*b*) (i) cholesterol would occupy site away from active site / bind to second binding site / bind to allosteric site
        or
        enzyme would not be destroyed / enzyme would be modulated
        or
        cholesterol / end product would interact with first enzyme in the sequence
        change in conformation / shape <u>and</u> reduced affinity for / binding of substrate (at active site)

        (ii) sits in active site <u>and</u> *any one from*:
        prevents substrate / HMG-CoA entering
        reduces available enzyme
        reduces mevalonate (for next stages)

        (iii) ML-236B is most effective inhibitor
        or
        Rank order in terms of effectiveness

        Quantify
        ML-236A does not reach on scale shown
        ML-236C at about 0.085 (+/- 0.005)
        ML-236B at 0.01

6. (*a*) (role of MPF is) to control entry into mitosis

   (*b*) Exit from mitosis / Entry to anaphase

      Ensures equal distribution of DNA / chromosomes

   (*c*) M cyclin increase, (enough) enzymes have been activated to pass checkpoint 2 / to enter mitosis
      or
      Decrease in M cyclin activates enzymes for passing checkpoint 3 / to enter anaphase / to exit mitosis

7. (*a*) (i) has two copies of fragment with 2 units
        or
        inherits fragment size 2 from both parents / both sets of grandparents

        (ii) <u>A and</u> Grandparents R and S do not have 4 or 1 / either of A's alleles
        or
        A does not have 5,3 or 2 so not related to R and S

   (*b*) probe identifies/ labels/tags the DNA fragments (in the gel)

8. A (*a*) **plant production by tissue culture**
      A maximum of five from:
      1. aseptic techniques / conditions
      2. named suitable medium eg (M+S)
         or two components: sugar, mineral (salts) / salts, N source, vitamins, amino acid, 'hormones'
      3. explant or protoplasts needed **or** description of source
      4. callus forms **or** mass of undifferentiated cells form
      5. growth regulators cause differentiation / formation of roots/shoots
      6. (plant growth regulators are) auxin **and** cytokinin
      7. plantlets from callus
      8. plant cells are totipotent / capable of differentiation into any cell type

   (*b*) **the use of *Agrobaterium***
      A maximum of four from:
      9. (transgenic defined) organism with genetic material of another organism
      10. (*Agrobacterium*) causes tumours / causes crown gall in plants
      11. disease is caused by (Ti) plasmid
      12. plasmids are (additional) circular DNA in bacteria
      13. the bacterium / its plasmid can be used to transfer DNA / can be a vector
      14. (*Agrobacterium* / Ti) plasmid inserts into (plant) DNA

   (*c*) **modification of plasmids**
      A maximum of six from:
      15. desirable gene removed / cut from source DNA
      16. (*Agro* / Ti) plasmid cut using endonuclease / restriction enzyme
      17. use same endonuclease / restriction enzyme OR reference to same sticky ends
      18. foreign DNA / gene joined to (Ti) plasmid DNA by ligase
      19. modified plasmid returned to (*Agro*)bacterium
      20. plasmid has marker gene / antibiotic resistance gene / or other example
      21. that allows only modified *Agrobacterium* / <u>bacteria</u> to grow
      22. plant cells are 'infected' with bacterium containing engineered plasmid
      23. **plant cells** (grown) in selective medium
      24. medium only allows growth of plant cells with foreign DNA
      25. role of Bt toxin as insecticide

8. B (*a*) **membranes**
      A maximum of five from:
      1. (membrane) proteins are integral / intrinsic and peripheral / extrinsic

2. integral /intrinsic = in membrane / (phospholipid) bilayer OR peripheral = on membrane
3. join cells OR form junctions
4. attach to cytoskeleton / extracellular matrix
5. transport of (hydrophilic) substances across membranes
6. **two** from carriers/channels/pumps
7. some membrane proteins are enzymes
8. glycoproteins / proteins with carbohydrate portion are for cell-cell recognition / are antigenic markers

(b) **cell signalling**
A maximum of five from:
9. some signalling molecules /hormones are proteins / peptides
10. hydrophilic signals cannot cross the membrane
11. protein / receptor for hydrophilic signal is in the membrane
12. receptors cause transduction / trigger cell response
13. hydrophobic signals / steroid hormones can pass through the membrane
14. protein / receptor for hydrophobic signals / steroid hormones is in the cell or in nucleus
15. protein / receptor is gene regulatory OR receptor-signal complex regulates transcription

(c) **cytoskeleton**
A maximum of five from:
16. cytoskeleton is made of (protein) fibres (of different types)
17. microtubules are made of tubulin / dimers / globular proteins
18. **microtubules** are straight / hollow rods
19. **microtubules** radiate from MTOC / centrosome
20. spindle fibres are microtubules
21. microtubules / cytoskeleton role in location / movement of (membrane-bound) organelles
22. cytoskeleton role in support / shape / movement of cells
23. other protein filaments in cytoskeleton + example keratin / intermediate or actin / microfilament
24. function of other component, eg actin in cytokinesis, keratin as fixed structure

SECTION C: BIOTECHNOLOGY

1. (a) (i) time for the cell number to double

(ii) generation time is shortest in broth
or
growth in broth is fastest / minimal media gives slower growth
carbon sources differ in their effects on growth rate / generation time

(b) $0.35h^{-1}$ (0.3465) **or** $0.0058min^{-1}$ (0.006)

(c) (i) *Any one from:*
(turbidity measurement) counts dead cells as well as live
not a viable count
cells of different shape / size scatter light differently
instrument has to be calibrated for each microbial species

(ii) dilution plating / haemocytometer / direct counting

2. 1. grass put in silos / wrapped in polythene
or
storage prevents air entry
2. (cut grass / silage) inoculated with *Enterococcus* and *Lactobacillus*
3. (and) cellulases / pectinases
4. enzymes (partially) break down cells / release nutrients

5. bacteria create anaerobic conditions
6. bacteria produce lactic acid which lowers pH
7. anaerobic conditions and low pH prevent growth of spoilage organisms
8. nutritional quality preserved

3. (a) (i) true for apple v soyabean *and* apple v wheat bran
no difference between apple pomace and cottonseed
or
no significant difference between apple pomace and cottonseed

(ii) reduces cost **or** gives high yield (of antibiotic)
gets rid of / upgrades waste

(b) bactericidal kill bacteria <u>and</u> bacteriostatic inhibit their growth / block their metabolism

4. (a) enzyme   organism
cellulase   *Penicillium* / *Aspergillus*
pectinase   *Erwinia*
amylase   *Bacillus subtilis* /*Aspergillus*

(b) (i) *Any two from:*
sterility
nutrient supply / concentration
oxygen supply / aeration
pH
temperature
addition of anti-foaming agents

(ii) *Any one from:*
flocculation
filtration
centrifugation
ultrafiltration
vacuum evaporation
chromatography

(c) substance produced in stationary phase (of population growth)
or
substance not required for the growth of the organism

SECTION C: ANIMAL BEHAVIOUR

1. (a) at low courtship frequencies large males are chosen more often / have a higher probability of mating but this reverses at higher frequencies
or
it changes from large males to small males as courtship rates increase

(b) (i) <u>latency</u>

(ii) <u>duration</u>

(c) <u>sexual dimorphism</u>

(d) less easy for predators to see them
may be nesting / laying eggs
or
survival chances of the young increase

2. (a) short lifespan so no time for learning
or
little or no parental care of offspring

(b) (*per* gene in *Drosophila*) controls 24 hour cycle / circadian rhythm

affects the amount of (PER) protein that is produced in the fly

or

different alleles / forms / mutations of the gene produce protein that alters the cycle

3. **For max net energy gain, need**
   Any five from:
   1. energy gain is from food intake
   2. energy loss is from searching / handling
   3. behaviour that maximises gain and minimises losses
   4. behaviour / prey selection that reduces / optimises handling time
   5. behaviour that increases encounter rate **or** decreases search time
   6. optimal foraging is maximising <u>net</u> energy gain
   7. predation strategies affect energy intake
   8. (benefit of) solitary hunting, predator gets all energy
   9. (benefit of) cooperative hunting – one from:
      individuals expend less energy foraging
      can take bigger prey
      have higher success rate

4. (*a*) improves survival chances of others

   cost to self in drawing attention of predator

   (*b*) mixed species / individuals are not related

   (*c*) the caller distracts other birds and will steal food
   or
   more food for caller if other birds move away

   (*d*) <u>comparison</u> needed, for example:

   fewer babblers responded to the false alarm (than to the true alarm)

   fewer babblers moved away when false calls were used

   (*e*) to remove the possibility that learning or habituation might arise
   or
   to make the data independent of each other
   or
   (good sampling technique) to assess range of variation between individuals in the population

SECTION C: PHYSIOLOGY, HEALTH AND EXERCISE

1. (*a*) *Any two from:*
   Formation of atheroma / plaque in walls of <u>coronary</u> arteries
   or atherosclerosis in <u>coronary</u> arteries

   Rough surface of wall allows clot formation

   Narrow lumen + leads to angina
   or
   Clot / embolus causes myocardial infarction

   (*b*) *Any two from:*
   smoking
   physical activity / exercise
   diet
   obesity

   (*c*) Physical activity decreases CHD
   or
   Postmen are more active than office workers <u>and</u> have lower CHD rate
   Age increases incidence (regardless of physical activity)

2. *Any four from:*
   1. (In osteoporosis) bone density / mass decreases
   2. weight bearing exercise increases bone density / mass
   3. example of weight bearing exercise
   4. maximum bone density is reached by mid 20s to 30
   5. exercise beyond 30 / by older people maintains bone density /delays decline
   6. exercise intensity needs to be moderate / should not be extreme
      or
      osteoporosis in young women associated with extreme levels of training

3. (*a*) (i) *Any one from:*
   to assess health risk
   to measure proportion of body fat
   to assess effect of dietary modification
   to assess effect of exercise training

   (ii) mass and volume

   (*b*) can misclassify individuals with a high muscle mass / lean tissue mass (as obese)
   or
   does not distinguish between muscle and fat mass (ie. does not assess composition)

   (*c*) (i) Male = 45; Female = 32

   (ii) BMI of 27 (correlates to) 36 %

   BAI gives 29·79 / 29·8 / 30%

4. (*a*) *Any two from:*
   Increased stroke volume
   Increased cardiac output
   Increased maximum heart rate
   Lower resting heart rate / HR during exercise

   (*b*) (i) *Any one from:*
   Increased / high **pre-exercise** muscle glycogen concentration gives increased endurance / exercising time to exhaustion

   (ii) <u>Maximal</u>

   (iii) cardiac patient rehabilitation
   assessment of heart disease
   elderly / unfit / untrained

BIOLOGY ADVANCED HIGHER 2014

SECTION A

1.	D	14.	D
2.	C	15.	C
3.	A	16.	D
4.	B	17.	B
5.	B	18.	D
6.	A	19.	B
7.	B	20.	B
8.	C	21.	D
9.	C	22.	A
10.	A	23.	C
11.	D	24.	A
12.	A	25.	C
13.	B		

SECTION B

1. (a) (in RM) **glucose transport** is higher in control / before insulin / after insulin

    or

    (in RM) **glucose transport** shows greater *increase*
    One correct quantification in support, eg 4 − 3

    (b) (i) (in the two cell types)
    amounts of GLUT / samples / tissue / fractions can be different

    (ii) Error bars overlap so differences (between GLUT levels) are not significant / (GLUT) levels could be the same

    (c) (i) All in PM / none in IM **in both types**

    (ii) (GLUT 1 stays in PM, so insulin has)
    no effect
    (on location / distribution / fraction / in either muscle type)

    (iii) (in both muscle types)
    insulin increases the amount of GLUT 4 in PM **and** decreases it in IM

    (d) (after insulin **both** muscle types have)
    (In Fig 4): **similar** (relative) **increase** in PM and (relative) **decrease** in IM

    (Fig 3): (comparing overall blot densities)
    bigger / darker blots in red muscle (1-4) than white (5-8)

    (e) (i) (hydrophilic signals)
    bind to a membrane receptor / membrane protein

    Only some / target cells have the receptors / specific proteins

    (ii) Signal at the outside / extracellular signal / insulin triggers a response inside the cell.

    (f) (i) Energy storage

    or

    storage (of glucose) in form that is **insoluble** / avoids osmotic effects

    (ii) Branched / polysaccharide / chains (of glucose molecules) / polymer

    and

    ∝ (1, 4) **glycosidic** bonds (between glucose molecules)

    or

    ∝ (1, 6) **glycosidic** bonds at branch points

    or

    Annotated diagrams

2. *Any four from:*
    1. Define transgenic as containing DNA from a different **species**
    2. **Ti plasmid** removed (from the bacterium)
    3. Tumour / gall causing "gene" removed / disabled
    4. desired gene extracted from source
    5. endonuclease /restriction enzyme cuts plasmid

    or

    source
    6. ligase seals/joins gene into plasmid
    7. incorporation of marker genes / antibiotic resistance genes / kanamycin resistance genes
    8. (modified) plasmid returned to *Agrobacterium*
    9. (*Agro*)bacterium incubated with protoplasts in selective medium

3. (a) Prosthetic (group)

    (b) (i) (origin) MTOC / centriole / centrosome **and** centromere / kinetochore

    (ii) to pull chromatids / chromosomes / centromeres apart

    (c) (i) *Both points*
    will fail to **align** chromosomes on the equator / metaphase plate
    because
    microtubules do not grow (enough to form spindle fibres)

    or

    microtubule growth is blocked

    (ii) Will affect **all** cells that are **dividing**

4. (a) covalent modification / proteolytic cleavage

    (b) Hydrolysis

    (c) prevents digestion of the pancreas / proteins in the pancreas

    or

    prevents digestion of other enzymes in pancreatic juice

    (d) trypsin can attack (the trypsinogen) at lysine and make more trypsin **that will do the same**

    or

    new trypsin can join in activation and speed up the conversion of trypsinogen

5. (a) (i) (requires) energy

    (ii) Extended / wide range of **habitats** / environments

    or

    Extends the range of temperatures inhabited

    (b) Osmoconformers

6. (a) to kill pests / reduce pest population **and** increase yield / reduce loss / reduce damage / that eat the crop

    (b) specific / biodegradable / not persistent

    (c) (i) 200%

    (ii) (*pairs of sentences with suggestion and corresponding reason*)
    eg
    smaller fields
    because
    bumblebees will get food within range of their nests / bumblebees can then forage beyond the monoculture

    or

    Increase diversity of flowering plants available
    because
    bumblebees do not store much food
    bees won't live long after the crop is harvested
    bees have longer to feed

7. (a) mutualistic relationship between coral (polyps) and algae / zooxanthellae

algae expelled from / leave coral
(and coral 'bleaches' / dies as temperature rises)

(b) (i) increases from about 24°C to 27°C around week 10 **then decreases**

(ii) (the spike caused a)
decrease in the floating canopy (seaweed) **and** increased the turf-forming / sea-bed cover

(c) allogenic succession

8. EITHER A or B.

A (i) *Maximum of six from:*
1. ecosystems depend on energy from the sun
2. autotrophs convert simple / inorganic molecules into (complex) organic molecules
3. (photo)autotrophs / producers convert **light to chemical energy by photosynthesis**
4. only a proportion of light energy available is fixed
5. productivity is **rate of** accumulation of biomass / organic matter
6. GPP = total energy fixed **or** total yield of organic matter/biomass (by photosynthesis)
7. NPP = energy remaining after respiratory losses **or** NPP = GPP − R
8. NPP determines energy available for animals / heterotrophs / next trophic level
9. chemoautotrophs description should include idea of obtaining energy from inorganic molecules to make organic molecules

(ii) *Maximum of nine from:*
10. autotrophs / producers are first trophic level
11. (second trophic level) primary consumers / herbivores + eat producers / plants
12. (third trophic level) secondary consumers / carnivores + eat animals
13. energy transferred through trophic levels is **by feeding**
14. energy losses occur at a trophic level / at transfers
15. one example of loss from: excreted / egested / uneaten material / dead organism
16. (losses) result in **energy flow** to decomposers / detritivores / saprotrophs
17. ultimate energy loss as heat **or** reference to thermodynamics
18. ecological efficiency is the % / proportion of energy **transferred** to next level
19. (%) transfer / ecological efficiency is low / '10% rule'
20. energy flow represented by pyramid of energy / productivity
21. energy losses restrict number of trophic levels

or

B (i) *Any five from:*
1. fossil fuels are burned to release energy
2. (burning fossil fuels) releases gases
3. example of (gas released from burning): sulphur dioxide / nitrogen oxides / carbon dioxide
4. these (dissolve in atmospheric water to) form acid rain
5. acid rain lowers pH of water (in freshwater ecosystem)
6. (acid rain) dissolves minerals out of the soil / rocks which pollute fresh water
7. carbon dioxide from burning fossil fuels **enhances** greenhouse effect / causes global warming
8. pH drop **or** temperature increase (may) reduce species diversity / affect species distribution

(ii) *Any five from:*
9. toxic pollutants are substances that cause harm to organisms (in their ecosystem)
10. heavy metals **or** an example are toxic pollutants
11. DDT is a (toxic) insecticide / pesticide
12. **describe** source of toxic pollutant
13. persistent / non-biodegradable / not broken down
14. toxicity arising from biotransformation
15. bioaccumulation + build up in one organism / trophic level
16. biological magnification + build up in successive trophic levels

(iii) *Any five from:*
17. example of biodegradable organic pollutant (eg plant waste / paper waste / farmyard manure / sewage)
18. ... results in high biochemical oxygen demand / BOD
19. BOD as measure of oxygen required (by decomposers)
20. (pollutant / organic material) stimulates growth / increases population of bacteria ...
21. ... decrease in concentration of dissolved oxygen
22. species which require high oxygen levels are **susceptible** / die out
23. species which can cope with low oxygen levels are **favoured** / increase (in population)
24. relative abundance of such species used to indicate / monitor quality (of freshwater ecosystem)

SECTION C – BIOTECHNOLOGY

1. (a) dilution plating / colorimeter (turbidity) / haemocytometer

(b) diauxic growth

(c) (i) (protein) not bound to operator
or
(protein) bound to inducer / lactose
and
transcription of structural gene occurs
or
structural gene switched on

(ii) (protein) (bound to cAMP) binds (promoter of the) *lac* gene and stimulates transcription of structural gene

(d) **lag** phase for *lac* operon / takes **time** for the **production** of β galactosidase

2. *Any five from:*
1. chymosin used in cheese production / to change milk to curds and whey
2. produced as an alternative to traditional rennet
3. recombinant plasmid containing (calf) chymosin gene
4. introduced into suitable species of micro-organism / *E.coli* / yeast / *K. lactis* / *Aspergillus niger*
5. fermentation / culturing of the modified micro-organisms
6. requires sterile conditions
7. need to control nutrients / oxygen / pH / temperature / anti-foaming agents / time
8. recombinant enzymes / chymosin produced as secondary metabolite

3. (a) (i) myeloma (cells)
(make) **hybridomas** immortal / can divide **indefinitely**

(ii) using selective media

(b) monoclonal antibody binds to tumour
radioactive component destroys / damages cells

4. (a) ranges overlap if data for 35°C and 50°C and if the same times are compared

   (b) (i) some autolysates don't contain detectable RNA (suggesting it has all been broken down)

   (ii) 50°C for 30 hours
   autolysate contains the most partially degraded RNA (for GMP/IMP production)

   (c) type of yeast / age of culture / growth stage of culture / pH / salt treatment

SECTION C – ANIMAL BEHAVIOUR

1. (a) (i) Petrels choose/prefer odours of non-kin/unrelated birds.

      (ii) 16

   (b) *Any one from :*
   Maze thoroughly washed
   Maze covered / avoid observer effects
   Odour stimuli alternated between arms (eliminate bias)
   Wear disposable gloves / eliminate human odour etc.

   (c) *Any two from:*
   Inbreeding increases expression of disadvantageous / lethal recessive alleles
   Results in lower fitness / reduced breeding success
   Natural selection favours behaviours with greater reproductive success

   (d) Males (natal) dispersal

2. *Any three from 1–5:*
   1. Human activity results in rapid environmental change
   2. Example – destruction of habitat / house building
   3. (Adaptable species) may change **diet**
   4. (Adaptable species may change) **foraging behaviour**
   5. (Adaptable species may change) **habitat preference**

   Any two correct examples such as
   6. exploitation of rubbish dumps by (herring) gulls
   7. urban foraging by foxes
   8. urban nesting in (herring) gulls
   9. species other than fox or gull

3. (a) Immediate / physiological / environmental factor
   trigger stimulus / sign stimulus

   (b) Time from event / stimulus to response/behaviour

   (c) Different individuals carrying out **different** tasks

4. (a) (i) Learning is a change of behaviour based on experience that must be remembered

      (ii) *Any one from:*
      Irreversible / difficult to reverse
      Critical time period
      Object of attachment followed to exclusion of others
      Occurs rapidly

      (iii) Object of attachment / followed is usually parent
      and
      Provides food / shelter / protection from predators etc

   (b) (i) Error bar overlaps zero line

      (ii) They prefer mates of the same species as the foster father

      (iii) Zig-zag dance / swimming into nest / swollen belly / nudging tail etc.

SECTION C – PHYSIOLOGY, HEALTH AND EXERCISE

1. *Any five from:*
   (exercise)
   1. reduces BP / hypertension
   2. reduces risk of MI / stroke
   3. improves (blood) lipid profile / increase HDL:LDL
   4. reduces fat / cholesterol in arteries and the risk of atherosclerosis
   5. reduces body fat / obesity which is a risk factor
   6. decreases (resting) heart rate
   7. improves myocardial circulation / blood flow to heart
   and
   link to angina / oxygen supply / oxygen deficiency

2. (a) (i) % (body) fat

      (ii) depends on hydration level (of the body)
      overestimates (fat) in lean people
      underestimates (fat) in obese people

   (b) (i) Bone is **more** porous / bigg**er** pore size
      and trabeculae thinn**er**

      (ii) do **weight bearing** exercise
      or
      increase bone density when young / under 30

      (iii) menopause (in women) speeds up loss of bone density
      or
      decreasing oestrogen at menopause
      or
      females have lower bone density to begin with

3. (a) Physical activity **and** BMR

   (b) (i) Volume of **air** breathed (in known time) **and** change in O_2 content of breathed air

      (ii) does not measure heat
      derived from oxygen consumed (rather than measured in calorimeter)
      uses correlation / relationship between O_2 consumption and energy use

   (c) (i) 400 kJ/d (accept %)

      (ii) *Any one from:*
      bias removed
      allows placebo effect to be measured
      psychological influences on outcome are avoided

4. (a) (i) not to exhaustion / used to derive VO_{2max}

      (ii) oxygen uptake / used **and** body mass / weight

   (b) (i) A: Time to exhaustion is greater than control **pre-training**
      B: no (significant) change in time to exhaustion following training
      or
      for HIT group: error bar for pre-training overlaps error bar post-training

      (ii) HIT group showed **significantly** shorter *trial time after training*